TITANIUM AND TITANIUM ALLOYS

by

John L. Everhart

Associate Editor, Materials & Methods
Reinhold Publishing Corporation
New York, N. Y.

A REINHOLD PILOT BOOK

BOOK DIVISION

REINHOLD PUBLISHING CORP.

Also publishers of "Materials & Methods," Chemical Engineering Catalog, Chemical Materials Catalog, "Progressive Architecture," Advertising Management of American Chemical Society

330 West 42nd St. New York, U.S.A.

1954

PREFACE

In the few years since titanium became a commercial metal, hundreds of papers have been published dealing with the metal. These papers are scattered through the transactions of a number of scientific and technical societies and through many business publications. It is the purpose of this book to present a selective review of the work covered in these publications and to supplement it with information obtained from the producers of the commercial materials.

This book is intended for the engineer or designer interested in the possibilities of applying titanium in the solution of his problems. It is not intended for the producer of titanium. Only sufficient information is included on production to indicate the effects of melting methods on the properties. Neither will this book appeal particularly to those engaged in research and development for it deals almost exclusively with technology. The properties of pure titanium are covered briefly merely to furnish a background for a discussion of commercial materials. It is hoped that this survey will indicate the present state of knowledge of titanium technology and point to some of the directions in which progress can be expected.

Many papers have been read and abstracted in developing this book. Acknowledgment to individual authors is made in the text. However, much of the information on commercial materials has been obtained from company literature. I am indebted to E. I. du Pont de Nemours & Co., Mallory-Sharon Titanium Corp., Rem-Cru Titanium, Inc., Superior Tube Co., and Titanium Metals Corp. of America for supplying data on commercial titanium and its alloys.

Finally, it is a pleasure to acknowledge the assistance of my secretary, Miss Ruby Spector, who typed the manuscript and my wife, Helen, who prepared many of the graphs and helped read the proofs.

Westfield, N. J.,   JOHN L. EVERHART
February, 1954

CONTENTS

v

1. INTRODUCTION

The intense interest in titanium apparent at every technical meeting at which it is discussed, shows that many people believe it has great commercial potentialities. This belief is based on three factors (1) abundance of raw materials (2) location of ores and (3) properties of the metal.

Titanium is the fourth most abundant element having structural possibilities in the earth's crust. Only aluminum, iron and magnesium are more plentiful. The titanium content of the crust is estimated to be greater than the combined totals of copper, lead, tin, zinc, nickel and the precious metals.

Mere abundance, however, does not insure economical availability. Minerals must be concentrated into fairly large deposits containing sufficiently high metal values to permit economical extraction from the earth if they are to be considered ores. Known deposits of high grade titanium are sufficiently plentiful to insure a supply of the metal for many years.

The location of large commercial deposits within the borders of the United States increases the interest in a metal which has high strategic value. It is this fact which has induced the Government to encourage the development of large scale production quickly. Only because of this encouragement and financial assistance has production increased from a mere 2½ tons in 1948 to about 2300 tons in 1953.

This unusual interest in a metal only about five years old, commercially, is based also on its properties. Titanium lies roughly half way between aluminum and iron in density. On a strength/weight basis, it is superior to all other structural metals. In addition it has excellent corrosion resistance to many environments. Thus it becomes a metal of great commercial and military potentialities.

The future of titanium is largely dependent on the ability of the producers to overcome the handicaps of batch operation leading to nonuniform composition, to produce shapes of uniform quality and to develop suitable fabricating methods. All these must be achieved at prices which will make the metal truly competitive with other constructional materials. Prices will have to be reduced greatly, if titanium is to become a generally useful metal in a civilian as contrasted with a military economy. If relatively low prices are not achieved, titanium will remain a specialty metal.

Developments during the past year have indicated that many of these problems are being overcome. There has been considerable improvement in uniformity, fabrication methods have been improved, suitable machining procedures have been devised which greatly reduce this problem and joining methods are being perfected. Only price has failed to show an improvement. There was no reduction during the year 1953.

Occurrence

Titanium occurs, naturally, chiefly as rutile (TiO_2) or ilmanite ($FeTiO_2$). Most of the rutile is found in beach sands while the ilmanite is generally found in hard rock, although it is found also in sands.

Beach sands containing both of these ores are found throughout the world, the largest known sources being in Australia, India and Brazil. Deposits are found in the United States in various localities but only those in Florida are being operated on a commercial scale.

Hard rock deposits containing ilmanite are found throughout the world also. These vary in size and grade and the mere presence of ilmanite does not indicate usefulness. Large deposits containing at least 30 per cent of ore are necessary if mining is to be profitable. The Bureau of Mines estimates that the world's largest known deposit of titanium in eastern Quebec could be the source of at least 50,000,000 tons of titanium metal. The largest hard rock ilmanite mines in the United States are in upper New York state but other high grade ores have been found in Virginia and North Carolina and lower grade ores occur in at least a dozen states.

Because of the abundance of ores in this country

3

and Canada, titanium is one of the few metals which the United States will not have to import from overseas sources in the event of an all-out war. This is one of the major reasons for the intense interest being exhibited by the Defense Department in the development of metallic titanium. Known deposits of titanium ore in the United States alone can furnish an ample supply for industry far into the future.

Extraction from the Ore

Titanium is a highly reactive element and extraction of a grade sufficiently pure to be ductile is difficult. The metal reacts with the oxygen and nitrogen of the air and in the molten state also reacts with all known refractories. Thus many problems had to be solved in winning it. At present, extraction is a two stage operation.

In the first stage, it is necessary to obtain titanium dioxide either by beneficiation of rutile or by smelting ilmenite to obtain a slag of high titanium content. Subsequently the crude oxide must be purified. In the second stage, metallic titanium is produced from this basic raw material.

Several methods have been suggested for winning metallic titanium from its ores and some have been operated on a laboratory scale. There is only one being operated on a commercial scale at present. Basically, this is the Kroll process, although various modifications are in use by different organizations. The starting material is titanium tetrachloride obtained by heating titanium dioxide, mixed with carbon, in a stream of chlorine. Titanium tetrachloride is obtained as an impure liquid which is purified by redistillation. Generally the purified tetrachloride is reduced by reaction with magnesium although other metals such as sodium can be used. The crude metal must be further treated to obtain a product sufficiently pure to be ductile upon consolidation.

Until quite recently, this reduction was carried on as a batch operation, the quantity produced in a batch was small and there was considerable variation in quality from batch to batch. However, considerable improvement has been achieved and a continuous process has been developed which should further improve the uniformity and quality of the product. The metal obtained by this method is a spongy material which must be consolidated by melting or other means.

The decomposition of titanium iodide has been used also for the production of titanium. Thus far this method has only been employed on a small scale although attempts are in progress to develop a continuous process. Since the method requires the vaporization of the iodide and its subsequent decomposition, a rather slow reaction, it appears that it will always be a high cost operation. The metal produced by this process is the purest obtainable and will probably be used mostly for experimental work. At present iodide titanium costs many times as much as the chloride product.

Other processes based on the electrolysis of a fused electrolyte offer many advantages and have been investigated extensively. One of these has reached the pilot plant stage. However, this is a batch operation, not a continuous process, and therefore will not be as economical as is desirable. Research work aimed at finding a continuous electrolytic process continues. It is probable that a method of this type will be developed but at present, and for the near future at least, a large proportion, if not the major proportion of the commercial titanium produced in the world will probably be obtained by some modification of the Kroll process.

Melting

The spongy product of the reduction process must be consolidated in some manner. Originally, powder metallurgy techniques were employed and these procedures will still find a place in the production of small parts but, for most purposes, melting is required to produce the massive ingots needed for further working. Both arc and induction melting furnaces have been employed. This step has been one of the major stumbling blocks in the process and has been responsible for the production of non-uniform material with widely varying properties.

However, the rapidly developing technology has led to great improvements in the furnaces used. Ingots up to 1200 or 1400 lb are commonly produced and furnaces have been installed which permit the production of 4000 lb ingots. This increase in size of ingots has been particularly advantageous because it has permitted the use of larger scale rolling equipment with a resulting improvement in the physical uniformity of flat products.

Probably the major melting method employed at present is arc-melting in a water-cooled copper crucible using an inert atmosphere which is generally argon. Either nonconsumable electrodes of graphite or tungsten or consumable electrodes of titanium are used, the latter being favored because they reduce the possibility of contamination of the melt. Sponge is introduced into the crucible, an arc is struck between the sponge and the electrode and a pool of molten metal forms. This solidifies rapidly in contact with the crucible walls, more sponge is added and an ingot is built up gradually. The process has been improved by a procedure called skull-melting. In this modification, a layer of titanium is frozen against the copper crucible walls. This layer acts as the crucible in ingot production and improves the purity of the product. The principal disadvantage of this melting procedure is lack of uniformity in the product because the ingot is built up of layers.

One method of improving uniformity has been the blending of selected batches of sponge. Another method, which has been suggested by Van Thyne, Turner and Kessler, particularly for production of alloys, is double melting. They point out that in single melting processes, segregation occurs particularly of high density constituents because of the relatively small quantity of metal which is molten at one time and the consequent lack of time to obtain uniform distribution. Two methods are employed in double melting. In one a nonconsumable electrode furnace is used for the first operation and the resulting ingot is forged to rod and used as a consumable electrode in the second operation. Alternately, consumable electrode melting is used for both operations.

Some producers prefer induction melting to arc melting. It is claimed to be the most desirable method because the stirring effect achieved during operation of the furnace assists in producing homogeneous ingots. However, it is necessary to use graphite crucibles and some carbon pick-up from the crucible occurs. Thus induction melted titanium has a higher carbon content than arc-melted and this increase in carbon has undesirable effects on some fabricating properties.

The induction method is also claimed to be the only satisfactory method of remelting heavy as well as light scrap. The reuse of scrap is one of the major problems of the industry and in this application induction melting has a definite advantage over other procedures. Some producers predict that when a suitable refractory is found which will not react with titanium, induction melting will probably supplant arc melting.

It has been suggested that the following carbon contents can be considered typical of the products produced by the different melting procedures (1) Arc-melted ingot produced with a consumable electrode, 0.03 per cent carbon; (2) arc-melted with a tungsten electrode, 0.05 per cent carbon; (3) arc-melted with a carbon electrode, 0.2 per cent carbon; and (4) induction melted, 0.6 per cent carbon.

Production

There have been many predictions of the rate of increase in production of titanium and most of them have been far too high.

Actually progress has been slow but steady. The first commercial metal was melted in 1948 and the

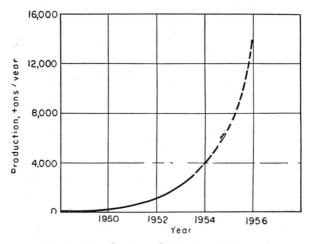

Fig. 1-1. Production of Titanium (Lippert)

output was about 5000 lb. By 1951, production had reached 500 tons and in 1953 this had increased to about 2250 tons. With new capacity both in the production of sponge and in melting about to go into operation, the figures may well be 7000 tons in 1954 and 13,000 tons in 1956. This is considerably

9

below the predicted 22,000 tons by 1955 but is far nearer the output expected by those in close touch with the industry than the higher figure.

In the meantime, demand is increasing and it is probable that titanium will be in extremely short supply until 1956 at least. Although there will be moderate quantities available for civilian aircraft and the development of other civilian applications, most of the material will be employed in the military program.

Production figures do not tell the whole story, either. It is estimated that 2 lb of sponge are required to yield 1 lb of rolled sheet and this high scrap loss reduces the material available for use. Until recently, most of this scrap has been stored because of inability to remelt the material. However, methods of reusing scrap have been devised. It is estimated also that 40 per cent of the titanium produced is scrapped at aircraft manufacturers' plants and much of this material is going to waste because it is not being segregated and returned to the mills.

The problem of scrap accumulations at manufacturers' plants has become so serious that the Business and Defense Services Administration has been requested to issue an order calling for the segregation of scrap since titanium has been declared a scarce material essential to military programs.

The slow rate of increase in titanium production is causing considerable anxiety in the Defense Department because of the lead-time necessary in aircraft design. At a recent meeting of a Senate Committee investigating strategic materials, it was brought out that the 1953 Air Force aircraft program called for 3500 tons of titanium while only about 2300 tons were produced, thus leaving a shortage for this application alone of more than 1000 tons. It was also pointed out that the minimum requirements for the Air Force in 1956 will be 35,000 tons but under the present program, scheduled output is only 25,000 tons, and actual output will probably be half as much.

These requirements cover only the needs of the Air Force. The Army and Navy could also use titanium in considerable quantities if it was available. Thus, the three services could use to great advantage more than 100,000 tons each year and because of civilian applications, it was suggested that the production goal should be 200,000 tons per year.

One of the bottle-necks in the attempts to increase production is the reluctance of producers to expand their production facilities using the high-cost Kroll process when they are hoping that a more economical process will be developed shortly.

In order to break this bottleneck, the Government will advance funds to producers to pay for increased capacity, guarantee to purchase most if not all of the sponge, allow quick tax write-offs and permit each company to cancel its obligation to the General Services Administration if the equipment becomes obsolete during the life of the contract. Theoretically, this expansion should increase the capacity to nearly 35,000 tons by 1957.

Economics

Titanium today is an expensive metal. Domestic sponge carries a price tag of $3 to $5 per lb. This figure when contrasted with the price of a few cents per lb for crude titanium dioxide reflects the cost of the Kroll process. It is claimed that the Japanese are able to produce sponge at a lower figure and they are actually delivering small quantities of the order of 5 tons per month in this country at about $400 per ton under the domestic price. However, the bulk of the sponge produced in this country, and as a matter of fact, in the free world will come from domestic producers for some years. Unless a lower cost process is introduced and brought rapidly into tonnage production, it is doubtful whether prices will fall much below $3 per lb in the near future.

When melting and mill charges are included, the prices of mill products such as sheet and rod range upward from about $10 per pound. One of the reasons for the high prices of mill products has been the inability to reuse scrap. However, two of the producers have developed procedures for remelting varying proportions of scrap and this development should result in a reduction in production costs which will be reflected in lower prices of these products.

Relative prices of Type 302 stainless steel, aluminum alloy 75S, magnesium alloy FS1 and titanium using several different bases are shown in Fig. 1-2. Since these metals are compared so frequently on a weight basis, a comparison of costs on the same base is interesting. One dollar will buy 18 times as much stainless steel, 60 times as large a volume of aluminum or magnesium or 200 times as much mild steel as it will buy in titanium.

With differentials such as this, a metal must have definite advantages if it is to receive any consideration for industrial applications. Gold is not chosen for an application where lead will serve equally

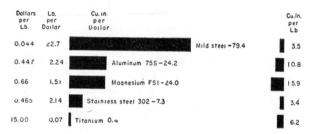

Fig. 1-2. Price-Volume Ratios for Several Metals in Sheet Form based on January 1954 Quotations

well but on the other hand, gold is chosen, in spite of the cost, if it has outstanding properties for a specific application.

Today this is the situation faced by titanium. There are many applications where titanium would be suitable if it were a cheaper metal but there are a few where cost is not so important. These are the applications in which titanium is making its first entry into the commercial field.

The most important of these applications is in the aircraft field and the designers of aircraft are definitely interested. The saving of a pound of weight in an airplane frequently is sufficiently important to justify using a high cost material. On these grounds titanium can and does enter the picture.

The Air Force considers that titanium is so important that a normal 10 to 20 year development

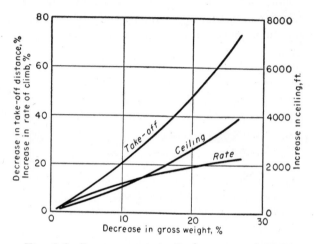

Fig. 1-3. Improvement in Performance of Fighter Planes through Decrease in Gross Weight (Adapted from *American Aviation*)

program must be compressed into a much shorter period. For this reason, the Government is not only buying the metal but also financing the production of the metal and its alloys, and the price is of relatively minor importance.

The major advantage of titanium results from the high strength/weight ratio. At room temperature

14

titanium shows little superiority over some of the stronger aluminum or magnesium alloys. However at slightly elevated temperatures, the light alloys lose strength rapidly while titanium retains much of its strength up to at least 800° F. Titanium and its alloys are also superior to stainless steels on the same basis in the range 300 to 800° F.

When it is considered that the saving of 1 lb in engine weight is equivalent to the saving of 8 to 10 lb in over-all weight, the reason for the interest shown by the Defense Department in titanium is apparent. Savings of this kind can be translated into increased range or greater maneuverability. Already incorporated to a minor extent in operating fighter planes and bombers, high performance supersonic airplanes now on the drawing boards call for 40 per cent titanium. Future plans call for as much as 60 per cent titanium, to cope with the increasing speeds demanded of the planes. At Mach 2 at 35,000 ft, it is estimated that skin temperature may reach 600° F. Neither aluminum nor magnesium can serve at temperatures of this order and stainless steel is too heavy, therefore titanium is required.

An indication of the high cost of using titanium in engine parts was given by Hanink, who points out that the major factor in parts cost differential lies in the high price of titanium. He estimated that it would cost upward of $50 per lb of weight saved to replace steel with titanium in an airplane engine.

Although it would appear that such high costs could be tolerated only for military aircraft such is not the case. Despite a cost of $15 per lb, titanium could be used profitably in commercial aircraft if it were available because of increased pay load. Thus a study made by the Douglas Aircraft Co. showed that the use of titanium in the engine nacelles and certain other parts of the DC-7 would reduce the weight sufficiently to allow an additional passenger to be carried. More extensive use of titanium would permit a 60-passenger plane to become an 80-passenger plane. An indication that this study was not purely academic is shown by the fact that titanium has been incorporated into certain components of the DC-7.

At present prices, titanium is also being given serious consideration for ordnance and other military equipment particularly that which will be airborne or be transported by the individual soldier.

The metal has proved sufficiently superior to others in resistance to certain corrosive environments to justify its use also.

However, extensive use in naval and marine applications, wide substitution for aluminum and magnesium alloys at moderate temperatures and competition with stainless steel in corrosion applications and other large tonnage applications will be delayed until the price of titanium is reduced substantially.

References

Van Thyne, R. J., Turner, D. H. and Kessler, H. D., "Double Melting Produces Homogeneous Titanium," *Iron Age*, 146 (Aug. 6, 1953).

Lippert, T. W., "Titanium in 1953," Titanium Metals Corp. of America (Dec. 30, 1953).

Anon., "New Planes Need More Titanium," *Aviation Week*, 22 (Nov. 23, 1953).

Hanink, H. H., "Application of Titanium to Aircraft Engines," *SAE Preprint No. 755* (April, 1952).

Anon., "Aircraft Manufacturers Reveal Plans to Use More Titanium," *Materials & Methods*, 7 (Jan., 1954).

Anon., "Problems Multiply in Structures Engineering," *American Aviation*, 38 (October 12, 1953).

2. HIGH PURITY TITANIUM

Although high purity titanium has no commercial significance, a knowledge of its properties is required to determine the effects of other elements which are present in the commercial material, either as intentional additions or as impurities.

The purest titanium available is produced by the iodide method. ASTM specification B266 places the following limits on this material

Titanium	99.9	per cent minimum
Carbon	0.03	per cent maximum
Silicon	0.02	per cent maximum
Iron	0.02	per cent maximum
Aluminum	0.03	per cent maximum
Nitrogen	0.01	per cent maximum
Manganese	0.04	per cent maximum
Others	0.01	per cent maximum

In addition, oxygen as determined by the vacuum method is less than 0.01 per cent, the specification stating that in the present state of the art it is not feasible to specify this element.

Iodide titanium has been used widely to investigate the properties of high purity material.

Physical Properties

Since titanium will compete chiefly with aluminum-base and iron-base alloys because of its properties, a comparison of some of the physical properties of the three elements points up the similarities and differences among them. (Table 2-1).

Table 2-1. COMPARATIVE PHYSICAL PROPERTIES
OF ALUMINUM, TITANIUM AND IRON

	Aluminum	*Titanium*	*Iron*
Density, Lb/Cu In.	0.10	0.16	0.28
Melting Point, F	1220	3020	2802
Thermal Cond, Btu/Hr/Sq Ft/Ft/F	126	8	46
Coeff of Thermal Exp per F	12.7×10^{-6}	5.0×10^{-6}	6.5×10^{-6}
Spec Ht, Btu/Lb/F	0.23	0.13	0.11
Elect Res Microhm-Cm	2.65	54	9.7
Mod of Elast, Psi	10,300,000	16,000,000	28,500,000

The melting point of titanium is several hundred degrees above that of iron and over 2½ times that of aluminum. The high melting point which, during the early stages of development seemed to promise alloys for high temperature service has so far failed to fulfill that promise. However, this failure can be traced to the reactivity of the metal at high temperatures and may be overcome in time by some form of surface treatment.

19

The density of titanium is intermediate between those of aluminum and iron. The modulus of elasticity, somewhat more than half that of iron, falls within the range of the copper alloys and is considerably higher than that of aluminum.

Thermal conductivity is low, being about 1/6 that of iron and 1/16 that of aluminum. Low thermal conductivity requires consideration in heating

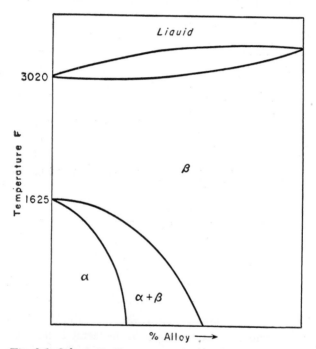

Fig. 2-1. Schematic Constitutional Diagram for Titanium Alloys (Finlay, Bradford and Fraser)

for fabrication at elevated temperatures and for welding.

The coefficient of expansion of titanium is somewhat less than that of iron while aluminum expands about 2½ times as much for equal temperature changes.

Electrical resistivity is about 6 times that of iron and 20 times that of aluminum. Thus titanium has a resistivity which approaches that of 18:8 stainless steel.

Most of these physical properties are not greatly affected by the small quantities of impurities present in commercial material. This, of course, does not apply to either electrical resistivity or thermal conductivity which are quite sensitive to impurity content. With the mechanical properties, however, there is quite a change.

Mechanical Properties

The mechanical properties of high purity titanium are given in Table 2-2. These properties, determined on iodide titanium show a tensile strength of 43,000 psi, an elongation of 40 per cent and a hardness of 105 on the Vickers scale. Roughly, this

Table 2-2. Mechanical Properties of Annealed Pure Titanium

(Jaffee, Ogden, Maykuth)

0.2% Offset Yield Strength Psi	27,000
Tensile Strength Psi	43,000
Elongation % (1 in.)	40
Reduction of Area %	61
Vickers Hardness (10 Kg)	105

21

puts the material into the same strength and ductility range as some of the annealed copper alloys although titanium is harder.

These mechanical properties have served as a base for the study of improvements achieved by alloying. The effects of small additions of some elements is indicated by the fact that in commercial titanium the strength is almost twice that of iodide titanium and the ductility is approximately half although the impurity content is still quite low.

Effects of Impurities

Hardness is frequently used as a criterion of the purity of titanium since it is quite a sensitive indicator. Westbrook has shown the relationship between titanium content and hardness. Although the nature of the impurities was not stated, these data

Table 2-3. Effect of Purity on Hardness
(Westbrook)

Titanium %	Vickers Hardness
99.95	90
99.8	145
99.6	165
99.5	195
99.4	225

were obtained on different lots of sponge and presumably the principal impurities were carbon, iron, oxygen and nitrogen. Table 2-3 shows that a difference of ½ per cent in impurity content makes a difference of 135 points on the Vickers scale.

Titanium readily absorbs carbon, nitrogen and oxygen and all three greatly affect the mechanical properties. Since one of the major problems in commercial production is the control of these elements, much work has been done on investigations of their effects. Finlay and Snyder have determined the mechanical properties of iodide titanium to which car-

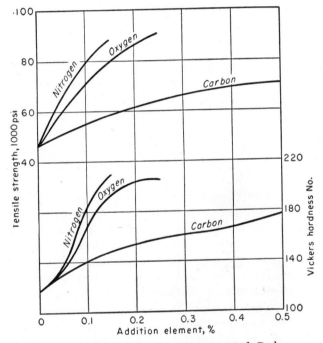

Fig. 2-2. Effect of Oxygen, Nitrogen and Carbon on the Strength and Hardness of Titanium (Finlay and Snyder)

23

bon, oxygen and nitrogen were added individually. The effects of small additions are shown in Fig. 2-2.

Of the three elements, nitrogen has the greatest strengthening and hardening effect, carbon the least. An addition of 0.15 per cent nitrogen almost doubles the tensile strength, and increases the Vickers hardness by 100 points. Ductility decreases with increase in all three elements.

This is further indicated by the work of Kinsey. His work (Table 2-4) shows that with an increase

Table 2-4. Effect of Oxygen and Nitrogen on the Properties of Annealed Titanium (Kinsey)

| Composition % | | Tensile Str Psi | Yield Str Psi | Elong % | Red of Area % | Vickers Hardness |
Oxygen	Nitrogen					
0.15	0.02	80,000	70,000	25		200
0.41	0.07	142,000	140,000	22	34	300
0.47	0.09	153,000	150,000	12	10	310
0.62	0.14	101,000	101,000	0	0	360

of both nitrogen and oxygen content, the hardness increases rapidly and the ductility as measured by elongation and reduction of area falls off sharply.

More recently, Simmons and Edelman have investigated the mechanical properties of cast titanium-carbon alloys to determine the possibilities of producing ductile castings by induction melting since at present graphite is the only practical material for handling titanium in the induction furnace. The carbon pick-up from the graphite crucible was sufficient to prevent the production of ductile castings by this method. The ductility as measured by the elongation fell off from 29 per cent to a low of about 1 per cent when the carbon content was increased from 0.04 to 0.9 per cent.

These investigations make it clearly evident that low contents of oxygen, nitrogen and carbon are necessary if ductile titanium is to be obtained. To point up the necessity for control, it should be noted that these are elements, which, once they have been dissolved in titanium, cannot be removed by any method known at present.

At temperatures above 600° F large quantities of hydrogen can be absorbed by titanium. Ultimately titanium is embrittled by this treatment. Unlike oxygen and nitrogen, however, absorbed hydrogen can be removed by heating the metal in a vacuum at elevated temperatures.

Iron is another common impurity in titanium but its effect is much less drastic than those of the elements mentioned above. Finlay and Snyder reported that the tensile strength of iodide titanium increased only from 42,000 to 60,500 psi with an addition of 0.5 per cent iron while the Vickers hardness number increased from 118 to 140. In this range the effect on ductility as measured by the elongation was moderate also.

Alloying

Like iron, titanium has a different structure at room temperature than it has at high temperatures. Unlike iron, in which these structures are called ferrite for the low temperature modification and austenite for the high temperature phase in technical practice, the titanium structures are known only by their metallographic designations, alpha and beta.

Alpha titanium has an hexagonal structure which is stable up to 1625° F. At 1625° F, the material changes to the high temperature modification which has a body-centered cubic structure and is known as beta titanium.

An accompanying schematic diagram (Fig. 2-1) for titanium alloys illustrates the fact that, as the content of certain alloying elements is increased, the lowest temperature at which the body-centered beta structure is stable decreases until finally this structure is stable below room temperature. This diagram shows also that there are three alloy types which can be obtained in titanium alloys, alpha, beta, and mixed alpha and beta.

All but one commercial alloy in production to date have mixed alpha and beta structures. The single exception is an all-alpha alloy which is just entering the commercial field. The all-beta alloys can be neglected for the present although they could become important in the future. Table 2-5 developed by Finlay, Bradford and Fraser, gives the advantages and disadvantages of these three types of structure and indicates that each will have a definite place in the future applications of titanium alloys.

Much work has been done in the development of constitutional diagrams for various binary alloys of titanium and sections of more complicated alloy systems have also been studied. A discussion of

Table 2-5. CHARACTERISTICS OF TITANIUM ALLOYS
(Finlay, Bradford, and Fraser)

All-Alpha Titanium Alloys

Advantages	Disadvantages
Useful strength to almost 1200° F.	Sheet bend ductility not as good as that of alpha-beta alloys; considerably poorer than that of beta alloys.
Resistant to air contamination to 2000° F, thereby permitting higher forging temperature.	Requires more power for hot working than alpha-beta.
No embrittling heat treatment response.	
Good weldability.	

Alpha-Beta Titanium Alloys

Advantages	Disadvantages
Double the strength of unalloyed titanium.	Heat treatment response (if not controlled results in loss of ductility.)
Good ductility, including bend.	Poorer weld ductility than alpha.
Forging, rolling and forming easier than alpha or beta. (Beta has better bend ductility.)	Temperature ceiling for useful strength about 800° F.
Relatively simple to produce in quantity.	
Heat treatable to higher strengths.	

Stable Beta Alloys

Advantages	Disadvantages
Excellent ductility in all forms (.020 sheet will bend flat on itself).	Very sensitive to contamination during production.
High strength useful to approximately 1000° F.	Sensitive to air contamination above 1300° F.
Does not require heat treatment for high strength.	High strength means greater springback in forming.
No heat treatment response.	Relatively high content of strategic alloying materials.

27

these diagrams is beyond the scope of this book. Much of the information has been published by the American Institute of Mining and Metallurgical Engineers, the American Society for Metals and the British Institute of Metals. A review published recently by Miller would be an excellent starting point for anyone wishing to pursue the subject further.

These investigations, however, have produced some very valuable information for alloy development by indicating the effects of various elements. One group promotes stability of the alpha, or low temperature, modification. This includes carbon, oxygen, nitrogen and aluminum. Another group promotes stability of the high temperature phase, and as mentioned previously, if present in large enough amount reduces the transformation on cooling below room temperature, thus making the beta phase the stable condition at ordinary temperatures. This group includes hydrogen, iron, manganese, chromium, molybdenum, and vanadium.

The effects of some of the more promising alloying elements on the mechanical properties serve to indicate the reasons for their selection to form commercial alloys.

Craighead, Simmons and Eastwood made an intensive study of the changes in mechanical properties produced in titanium when various elements were added to form binary, ternary and quaternary alloys. Fig. 2-3 shows the effects of a number of these elements on the tensile strength of binary titanium alloys. Although high purity titanium was not used, the investigation is valuable in indicating the effects of these elements alone, and in combination.

Their work indicates that vanadium produces a moderate increase in strength but there is some sac-

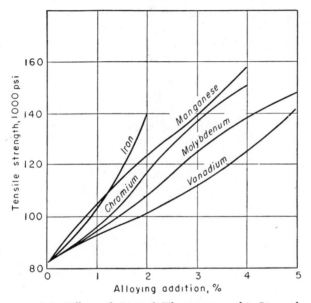

Fig. 2-3. Effect of Several Elements on the Strength of Titanium (Craighead, Simmons and Eastwood)

rifice in ductility. Chromium is one of the best of the addition elements for strength improvement but it reduces the ductility more than vanadium. Molybdenum has about the same effects as chromium, while manganese is also an excellent alloying element. Iron increases the strength to a greater degree than any of the metals mentioned previously but it also drastically reduces the ductility. These results with iron serve to point up the powerful effects of carbon, oxygen and nitrogen in small quantities, since iron is much less potent as a strengthening element than these elements.

In ternary alloys, these investigators found that the addition of 0.25 per cent carbon to the binary titanium-vanadium alloy had little effect on the properties. Similar results were obtained by adding carbon to several of the other binary systems.

The addition of 0.1 to 0.2 per cent nitrogen to the binary titanium-chromium alloys increased the hardness and strength but lowered the ductility to some extent.

Iron added to the binary titanium-manganese alloys increased the strength but lowered the ductility.

The quaternary systems studied included alloys based on chromium, carbon and nitrogen with the addition of several other elements. Tensile strengths up to 195,000 psi and Vickers hardness numbers up to 417 were obtained but ductility as measured by the elongation ranged from a low of 3 to a high of 9.5 per cent. Some of these alloys showed age-hardening properties.

All of the metals mentioned above have been introduced into alloys which are now in commercial production.

Aluminum is an alpha strengthening element and one of the two metals of this type now being used in a commercial alloy. The effect of aluminum on titanium has been studied by Ogden, Maykuth, Finlay, and Jaffee. They found that the tensile strength increased from about 42,000 psi at 0 per cent aluminum to 78,000 at 5 per cent while the

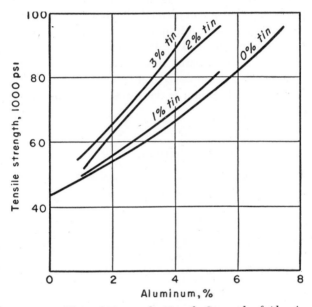

Fig. 2-4. Effect of Tin on the Tensile Strength of Aluminum Titanium Alloys (Rem-Cru)

ductility as measured by the elongation dropped from 60 to 19 per cent. Over the same composition range the Vickers hardness number increased from 100 to 200. This work was continued to high aluminum contents but these investigators concluded that the maximum workable content was 7.5 per cent aluminum.

The addition of another alpha-stabilizer, tin, to the titanium-aluminum alloys was investigated by Finlay, Jaffee, Parcel and Durstein. Some of their data are included in Fig. 2-4. The results were so promising that a commercial alloy containing these elements has been introduced recently. Iodide titanium on which most of the work covered in this chapter has been based is, at present, much too expensive to be employed on a commercial scale. Commercial titanium is discussed in the following chapter.

References

ASTM Standards Part 2, "Non Ferrous Metals," American Society Testing Materials, Philadelphia, 752 (1952).

Jaffee, R. I., Ogden, H. R. and Maykuth, D. J., "Alloys of Titanium with Carbon, Oxygen and Nitrogen," *Trans. AIME,* **188,** 1261 (1950).

Westbrook, J. H., "Temperature Dependence of the Hardness of Pure Metals," *Trans American Society Metals,* **45,** 221 (1953).

Kinsey, H. V., "Titanium—Its Physical Properties and Potentialities," *Canadian Mining and Metallurgy Bul,* **46,** 411 (1953).

Simmons, O. W. and Edelman, R. E., "Mechanical Properties of Cast Titanium-Carbon Alloys," *Amer Foundrymen's Soc.* preprint 53-48, 1953.

Finlay, W. L. and Snyder, J. A., "Effect of Three Interstitial Solutes (N,O, and C) on the Mechanical Properties of High Purity Alpha-Titanium," Trans *AIME,* **188,** 277 (1950).

Finlay, W. L., Bradford, C. I. and Fraser, G. T., "The ABC of Titanium Alloys," *Metal Progress*, 73 (Nov., 1952).

Miller, G. L., "The Investigation of Titanium Alloy Systems," *Industrial Chemist*, 202 (May, 1953).

Craighead, C. M., Simmons, O. W. and Eastwood, L. W., "Titanium Binary Alloys," Trans *AIME*, 188, 485 (1950).

Craighead, C. M., Simmons, O. W. and Eastwood, L. W., "Ternary Alloys of Titanium," Trans *AIME*, 188, 514 (1950).

Craighead, C. M., Simmons, O. W. and Eastwood, L. W., "Quaternary Alloys of Titanium," Trans *AIME*, 188, 539 (1950).

Ogden, H. R., Maykuth, D. J., Finlay, W. L. and Jaffee, R. I., "Mechanical Properties of High Purity Titanium-Aluminum Alloys," Trans *AIME*, 197, 267 (1953).

Finlay, W. L., Jaffee, R. I., Parcel, R. W. and Durstein, R. C., "Tin Increases Strength of Ti-Al Alloys Without Loss of Fabricability," *Jour. of Metals*, 25 (Jan., 1954).

Schofield, T. H. and Bacon, A. E., "The Melting Point of Titanium," *Jour. Institute of Metals*, 82, 167 (1953).

3. PROPERTIES OF COMMERCIAL TITANIUM

All commercial titanium contains carbon, oxygen and nitrogen in small quantities and all three of these elements exert great influence on properties. The actual content depends on the quality of the sponge and the melting procedure since it is impossible to improve the sponge quality by melting.

In the early stages of development, considerable confusion occurred because of the publication of widely different properties for material called "commercial titanium." With the increasing knowledge of the effects of carbon, oxygen and nitrogen on the mechanical properties, it was recognized that several grades of material were being included under a common designation and the product of one producer often differed widely from that of another. It was apparent also that much of the variation was related directly to the sponge. It was then realized that "commercial titanium" was actually a group of materials varying considerably in composition and properties. This led to a re-evaluation of early results and the initiation of programs to develop standards.

The ASTM has issued specifications for titanium ingot and mill products. Specification B264 sets up standard requirements for four grades of commercial titanium based on composition and hardness. Specification B265 covers the hardness, tensile and yield strengths required when the materials covered in the previous specification are supplied in the form of strip, sheet, plate, bar, tube, rod or wire.

Classification by yield strength was followed by the Ordnance Department in developing specification Mil-T-12117 (ORD). Sponge and metal are divided into six classes ranging in yield strength from 40,000 to 150,000 psi with the minimum allowable bend radius as an additional criterion.

The SAE has issued Aeronautical Materials Specifications AMS 4900, 4901, 4908, 4921 and 4925 for sheet, strip, bar and forgings.

Producers of sponge and mill forms also have developed specifications for their products, while certain consumers have developed company specification to be used in purchasing.

In these initial stages of standardization, it would seem to be important that all interested organizations unite in drawing up a set of standards which could be employed universally. Only in this manner will it be possible to avoid the endless confusion caused by the multiplicity of standards with which older materials are plagued. The ASTM, the SAE and the Ordnance Department are attempting to develop mutually agreeable standards at present.

Table 3-1. Composition of Commercial Titanium

Designation	Producer	Nominal Composition—%				
		C	O	N	Fe	Other
Ti-75A	Titanium Metals	0.07 max	0.20 max	0.10 max	0.20 max	Si, 0.02-0.04; H, 0.02-0.05; W, 0.02 max
RC-55	Rem-Cru	0.2 max	(a)	(a)	(a)	—
MST Grade III	Mallory-Sharon	0.25 max	—	—	—	—
RC 70	Rem-Cru	0.2 max	(a)	(a)	(a)	—
MST Grade IV	Mallory-Sharon	0.3-0.8	—	—	—	—
Ti-100A	Titanium Metals	0.07 max	0.30 max	0.10 max	0.30 max	Si, 0.02-0.04; H, 0.02-0.05; W, 0.02 max

^{a} Few hundredths to few tenths.

For the benefit of the user who might become confused with the variety of designations, one producer is now using the ASTM specifications to designate his products. It would advance the technology of titanium considerably if the other producers would agree to designate their materials by a series of mutually agreeable standard grades. At present, however, all other producers list their products by code numbers which, in the case of commercial titanium, are intended to indicate nominal yield or tensils strengths. The nominal compositions of commercial titanium are given in Table 3-1.

Physical Properties

In general, the physical properties of commercial titanium reported in the literature appear to be similar to those discussed in the previous chapter. Al-

Table 3-2. PHYSICAL PROPERTIES OF COMMERCIAL TITANIUM

Density, Lb/Cu In.	0.16
Melting Point, °F	3135
Thermal Cond, Btu/Hr/Sq Ft/Ft/°F at 212° F	8-10
Coef of Thermal Exp, F(68-1600° F)	5.0×10^{-6}
Specific Heat, Btu/Lb/°F	0.13
Elect Res, Microhm-Cm	55-65
Elect Cond, % IACS	2.7-3.1
Mod of Elast, Psi	16,000,000

though density varies slightly, the value 0.16 lb per cu in. applies to all grades for practical purposes. Single values also can be used for melting point, specific heat and coefficient of thermal expansion.

Typical values of these and other physical properties are given in Table 3-2.

On the other hand, conductivity is sensitive to the impurity content of the titanium and values of electrical resistivity have been reported ranging from 54 microhm-centimeters for ASTM Grade No. I to about 65 for ASTM Grade IV.

Reported values for the modulus of elasticity range from 14,000,000 to 20,000,000 psi. A value of 16,000,000 psi is probably as representative as any and is satisfactory for design purposes. Similarly, a modulus of rigidity of 6,000,000 psi and a Poisson's ratio of 0.33 will serve for designing with all grades of commercial titanium.

Mechanical Properties

Because of the variations in composition mentioned, it is not possible to give a single set of values for commercial titanium. The product of each producer is a different material. Nominal mechanical properties of the various commercial grades are given in Table 3-3.

The purest commercial grade, produced from specially selected batches of sponge, is available on a limited scale from several producers. This grade has a yield strength of about 55,000 psi while the ductility as measured by the elongation is about 20 per cent.

The most widely used grade has a nominal yield strength of about 70,000 psi while the increased impurity content reduces the elongation to values variously reported as 15 to 20 per cent. Compressive

Table 3-3. Mechanical Properties of Commercial Titanium

Designation	Form	Condition	Yld Str 0.2% Offset Psi	Ten Str Psi	Elong % 2 in.	Red of Area %	Hardness Rockwell	Hardness Brinell
RC-55	Sheet	Annealed	55,000[a]	65,000[a]	20	55	R_A 50-54	—
RS-55	Forgings	Annealed	55,000[a]	60,000[a]	20	—	R_B 90	—
Ti-75A	Sheet and Strip	Annealed	70,000[a]	80,000[a]	20[a]	—	R_B 85-95	190-240
	Plate	Annealed	55,000- 80,000	70,000-100,000	18[c]	45-50	—	—
	Wire	Cold drawn	65,000- 80,000	75,000- 90,000	8[c]	35-40	—	—
			120,000-130,000	140,000-150,000				
	Forgings and hot rolled bars	Annealed	60,000- 80,000	75,000-100,000	20-30[c]	—	—	235[b]
RC-70	Sheet	Annealed	70,000[a]	80,000[a]	15	50	R_A 54-58	—
	Sheet	Half Hard	105,000[a]	120,000[a]	12	35	R_B 102	—
RS-70	Forgings	Annealed	70,000[a]	80,000[a]	18[a]	—	R_A 60	—
MST Grade III	Sheet	Annealed	72,000	80,000	25	55	R_A 64	—
		Cold worked 50%	110,000	125,000	12	30	—	—
MST Grade IV	Forgings	As forged	72,000	80,000	25	55	R_A 62	—
	Sheet (0.040 in.)	Annealed	85,000	100,000	18	15	R_A 61	—
		Cold worked 37%	120,000	130,000	6	14	R_A 65	—
	Forgings	As forged (80% red)	75,000	80,000	18	50	R_A 61	—
	Forgings	Annealed	90,000[a]	100,000[a]	15[a]	—	Rc 30[b]	—
Ti-100A	Sheet and Strip	Annealed	85,000-115,000	100,000-120,000	15-22	—	—	250-290
	Plate	Annealed	80,000- 95,000	100,000-115,000	20[c]	—	—	—
	Wire	Cold Drawn	155,000-165,000	185,000-195,000	10[c]	45-50	—	—
	Forgings and hot rolled bars	Annealed	70,000- 90,000	90,000-120,000	15-25[c]	20-30	—	230-270

[a] Minimum. [b] Maximum. [c] Percent elongation in 4D, minimum.

yield strengths of the same order of magnitude as the tensile yield strengths have been reported.

Johnson and Hassell have compared the mechanical properties of this grade of titanium with some other materials on a strength/weight basis with interesting results. They report a yield strength/density ratio for annealed titanium of 428 compared with 490 for full hard type 304 stainless steel and 510 for 24S-T4 aluminum. The comparison is more impressive when made with annealed type 304 stainless. On this basis, the ratio of 428 for titanium compares with 105 for the stainless steel.

A third grade containing somewhat higher carbon than the others has a yield strength of 85,000 psi and an elongation about the same as the 70,000 psi grade.

It is difficult to determine when the content of an element passes from the impurity stage to attain the status of an alloying element in the popular sense of the word. Therefore another grade of titanium is included in this chapter. This material is called an oxygen-nitrogen alloy by the producer but appears to fit more nearly into the commercial material classification than into the alloys and has been so classified in this book. This material has a nominal yield strength of 100,000 psi and an elongation of about 15 per cent.

The investigations of properties other than those obtained on a tensile test have been made almost invariably on the grade having a nominal yield strength of 70,000 psi and specifically on RC-70 and Ti-75A. In the discussion which follows on other properties, commercial titanium implies the use of one of these two materials.

Titanium can be strengthened considerably by cold work. As can be seen in the table, strengths well over 100,000 psi can be reached by cold drawing. Of course the dutility is reduced considerably by such working. Fig. 3-1 shows the increase in strength and the accompanying decrease in ductil-

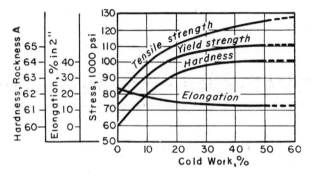

Fig. 3-1. Effect of Cold-Working on the Properties of RC-70 (Rem-Cru)

ity for one of the commercial grades produced by working to various reductions.

Fatigue Properties

When determined on polished specimens, the fatigue strength of titanium compares favorably with the steels. However, surface condition has considerable influence on fatigue. For example, cold working the surface of titanium decreases the fatigue strength which is in marked contrast with the improvement obtained when austenitic stainless steels are cold worked.

The influence of notches is the subject of considerable controversy. Some authorities believe that titanium is quite notch sensitive while others maintain that the notch sensitivity is no greater than that of the steels. Data are available to support each side of the argument. However, some of the work showing the most damaging effects of notches was done in the early days of production when the material was far from uniform and improvement should be expected with the improvement in quality of the material. Be that as it may the designer should not disregard the possibility of notch sensitivity in his calculations.

Table 3-4. EFFECT OF NOTCHES ON FATIGUE STRENGTH
(Spretnak, Fontana, and Brooks)

| Material | Tensile Strength Psi | Fatigue Strength Psi 10⁷ Cycles | |
		Un-notched	Notched
Titanium	89,600	73,500	27,500
24-ST Aluminum	69,900	25,500	11,000
75-ST Aluminum	83,900	30,000	15,000
FS1 Magnesium	40,100	19,000	8,000
SAE 4340 Steel	146,000	74,000	20,000
	231,000	89,200	49,000
Type 304 Stainless Steel	212,000	110,000	23,000

Note: 60 deg notch, depth 0.025 in., root radius 0.010 in.

Table 3-4 shows some of the data obtained by Spretnak, Fontana and Brooks in an extensive investigation of fatigue of various materials. They concluded that notches significantly reduce the fatigue strengths at room temperature of all of the

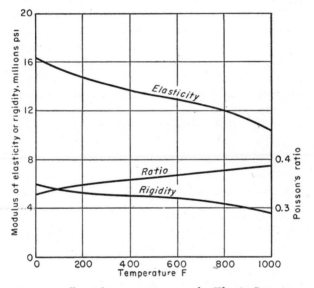

Fig. 3-2. Effect of Temperature on the Elastic Constants of Ti-75A (Titanium Metals)

metals tested. Their work indicates however that with the type of notch used, damage to commercial titanium is less severe than to stainless steel.

It is interesting to note that this work also indicates a much higher fatigue strength/tensile strength ratio for titanium than is commonly achieved in testing steels. Other investigators have found however that the fatigue strength of titanium is about ½ the tensile strength and thus lies in the same range as the steels.

For applications involving cyclic stresses under corrosive conditions, such as in contact with sea water, it seems to be generally agreed that titanium has excellent properties. Williams states that endurance tests run on commercial titanium have indicated that there is little difference in fatigue strength between samples tested in air and those tested in salt water and it is the only high strength structural material known which acts in this manner. He stated also that a fatigue test is a highly sensitive indicator of corrosion damage and the data obtained in the tests support the claims that titanium is outstanding in its resistance to corrosion in marine environments.

High Temperature Properties

When it was determined that titanium had a higher melting point than iron, great hope was held for its use in high temperature service. This hope has not been realized.

Titanium has a high affinity for oxygen and nitrogen and once these elements are absorbed, there is no known method of removing them. In sufficiently large quantities, they embrittle titanium. At room and moderately elevated temperatures, an oxide skin forms on the metal and protects it from further oxidation. However, at about 1000° F the metal begins to absorb this skin and at temperatures above

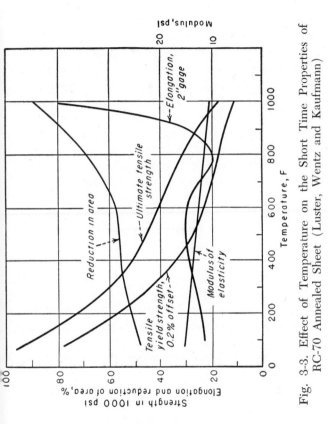

Fig. 3-3. Effect of Temperature on the Short Time Properties of RC-70 Annealed Sheet (Luster, Wentz and Kaufmann)

45

1400° F, the absorption is quite rapid. Walden and Dixon investigated the effect of short time heating in the temperature range 1200 to 2000° F on the properties and structure of titanium. They concluded that the metal can be exposed for a maximum of ½ hr at temperatures up to 1500° F in air. Above this temperature it becomes excessively brittle. Prolonged exposure of the metal to temperatures above 1000° F produces similar embrittlement. It should be noted that these results are based on tests on sheet material. Heavy sections of titanium are heated regularly in commercial operations to temperatures above 1500° F for forging and hot working. The rate of penetration of oxygen and nitrogen is low enough to limit damage to a skin which is removed subsequently.

For service at moderate temperatures in the range 400 to 800° F commercial titanium has interesting properties. A comparison of the strength with those of the aluminum alloys 24S and 75S shows that titanium loses strength at a much lower rate than the aluminum alloys. On a strength-weight basis, titanium is several times as strong at 700° F as these aluminum alloys and is equivalent to the 18-8 stainless steels.

The variation of the elastic constants with temperature in the range 80 to 1000° F is given in Fig. 3-2. These figures can be useful in design particularly in view of the peculiar behavior of titanium in long time tests.

Although short time properties are useful for an initial comparison of materials, it is necessary to

46

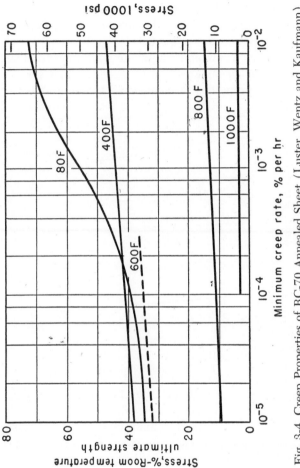

Fig. 3-4. Creep Properties of RC-70 Annealed Sheet (Luster, Wentz and Kaufmann)

47

investigate the effect of time at temperature if the material is to be used for service at elevated temperatures. This requires the determination of creep and stress-rupture properties.

Luster, Wentz and Kaufmann have reported the results of an investigation of the creep and stress-rupture properties of commercial titanium at tem-

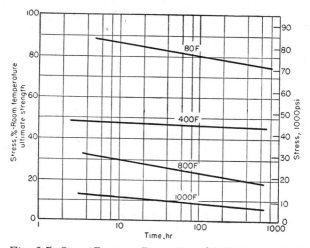

Fig. 3-5. Stress-Rupture Properties of RC-70 Annealed Sheet (Luster, Wentz and Kaufmann)

peratures from 80 to 1000° F. The work confirmed the previous investigations which had indicated that titanium showed definite creep at room temperature but did not show creep at about 600° F. Creep curves for commercial titanium at temperatures ranging from 80 to 1000° F and stress rupture curves are given in Figs. 3-4 and 3-5.

48

Low Temperature Properties

 Applications of materials at sub-zero temperatures are increasing in importance and the determination of low temperature properties has become commonplace in evaluating a new material because materials suitable for service near zero might be unsuitable at lower temperatures. Conditions of loading also determine usefulness. Under static loading a material suitable for room temperature service might be satisfactory at quite low temperatures. However, under shock loading, restraint or vibration, the tendency of some materials, notably certain steels, to become embrittled limits their low temperature applications.

In general the strength and hardness of titanium increases with falling temperatures, like the steels. The ductility as measured by the elongation drops rather sharply at the lower temperatures. There is some increase in stiffness also with falling temperatures.

One of the more sensitive indicators of resistance to shock is the impact test on a notched specimen. This test has been used frequently in evaluating the properties of titanium, and has produced some widely varying results. In one of the most comprehensive investigations, Spretnak, Fontana and Brooks have shown that the impact strength of commercial titanium drops significantly between $-110°$ F and $-321°$ F. Data on the change in properties between room temperature and $-321°$ F are given in Table 3-5.

Temperature F	77	−321
Mod of Elast, Psi	16.7×10^6	19×10^6
Yield Str (0.2% offset) Psi	72,000	177,000
Tensile Str, Psi	90,000	186,000
Elong % (4D)	27.5	13.8
Reduction of Area, %	24.0	14.8
Fatigue Str, (10⁷ cycles) Psi	73,500	100,000
Vickers Hardness No.	257.	414
Impact Test (Charpy, Keyhole notch) Ft-Lb	14.5	6.6

Corrosion Properties

One of the outstanding properties of titanium is its excellent resistance to corrosion. This property will undoubtedly lead to many applications in the future, a fact which is frequently lost sight of in the wide publicity being given to its suitability for service where weight is a factor.

The basis of its corrosion resistance is considered to be the formation of a protective surface film. This film formation is promoted by the presence of oxygen or oxidizing agents and thus titanium is quite resistant to attack by some reagents which are usually highly corrosive.

Marine Environments. Exposure of commercial titanium to sea water and salt air at the International Nickel Company's test stations showed that there was no significant attack in five years in any of the tests employed. Titanium becomes fouled with marine growths like many other materials but pitting and localized attack were not observed near the growths.

Williams reported the results of a rotating disk test employed to evaluate corrosion-erosion damage. This disk, 5 in. in diameter is rotated in sea water at a speed of 1140 rpm. In a test of this type, water velocity increases toward the periphery and for many materials there is a critical velocity beyond which protective films are swept away and accelerated corrosion occurs.

After a sixty day test, a titanium disk had lost only 0.05 grams in weight, no critical velocity was apparent, and there was no reduction in the thickness of the disk at the outer edge. The next best material in the test lost 4 grams, and the thickness at the edge was reduced by 0.003 in.

Williams also reported that in hydraulic cavitation tests designed to test materials to determine their suitability for use as marine propellers, titanium was exceeded in resistance only by cast 16 chromium-6 nickel steel in a group of eight materials.

These results indicate that titanium will find broad applications in the marine field when it is available at a competitive price.

General Corrosion. At room temperature, titanium shows excellent resistance to nitric acid in all concentrations. Even at elevated temperatures and pressures, the reaction with nitric acid is slow. Chromic acid acts similarly.

Resistance to sulfuric acid depends on the concentration. Titanium resists dilute acid but the rate of attack increases with concentration particularly in the presence of air. Hydrochloric acid attacks the metal slowly at room temperature. The rate increases with concentration and temperature. Rates of attack by both sulfuric and hydrochloric acids can be reduced greatly if traces of chromic or nitric acid are present.

All concentrations of hydrofluoric acid corrode titanium rapidly and common oxidizing agents do not reduce the rate.

Tests in alkaline solutions have shown that no significant attack occurs in ammonium hydroxide at room temperature and the rates of attack by dilute sodium or potassium hydroxide are extremely low. Titanium shows good resistance to hot solutions of sodium hydroxide in moderate concentrations.

Titanium has excellent resistance to moist chlorine gas and to water saturated with chlorine. It is resistant also to hot and cold chloride salts of all concentrations, with the exception of boiling solutions containing more than 25 per cent aluminium chloride. Worth noting are the low rates of attack by cupric and ferric chlorides since these are among the most corrosive solutions encountered in industry. Rates of attack on sodium and calcium hypochlorite solutions are also low.

In the field of organic materials, titanium has excellent resistance to hot and cold acetic, lactic, citric and stearic acids in practically all concentrations. It is practically unattacked by boiling solutions of many other organic compounds. These include carbon tetrachloride, trichlorethylene, formaldehyde and chloroform. Titanium is attacked rapidly however by hot oxalic and trichloracetic acids and by boiling concentrated formic acid solutions.

Galvanic Corrosion. Galvanic corrosion, which is faster than normal corrosion, occurs when two metals having different electrochemical potentials are in electrical contact and are submerged in an electrolyte. Under such conditions, the less noble metal corrodes more rapidly and the more noble metal corrodes less rapidly than they would if exposed to the same solution individually.

The possibilities of galvanic corrosion can be predicted by a study of the galvanic series obtained by arranging the metals in the order of increasing nobility. The nearer together two metals are in this series, the less effect they will have on each other if they are in contact in a corrosive medium.

Such a series developed for salt water corrosion places titanium toward the noble end of the series near passive 18-8 stainless steel. Thus the coupling of titanium with 18-8 stainless in salt water results in negligible attack on either metal. In tests in which titanium was coupled with less noble metals and exposed to salt water, the titanium was not damaged and the rate of attack on the second metal was similar to that resulting from a couple in which 18-8 stainless was used as the noble member of the couple.

Stress Corrosion. The corrosion resistance of titanium is attributed to the presence of a protective surface film. Metals which owe their resistance to such a factor are usually susceptible to stress corrosion cracking because breaks in the film offer points of attack.

Kiefer and Harple have investigated the attack on titanium of a number of standard solutions used for the stress corrosion testing of other metals. No cracking occurred on highly stressed titanium samples in a series of over twenty reagents of this type even after several weeks exposure. Particular mention was made that no cracking occurred in 20 per cent ferric chloride solution at room temperature.

The only reagent they found which did cause cracking was red fuming nitric acid. On totally immersed samples cracking occurred in from 3 to 16 hr while samples held in the vapor cracked after several weeks exposure. It should be mentioned that in stress-corrosion testing with red fuming nitric, explosions have occurred when test bottles were opened after several weeks exposure. Therefore caution is advisable when making this test.

It should be recognized that these corrosion results are only indicative of the resistance of titanium to corrosion and they should be regarded merely as a preliminary guide to applications. Rates of corrosion are affected so greatly by purity of solution, aeration, flow of the liquid and other factors that no specific recommendations are possible. An actual test under operating conditions is desirable.

References

"Nonferrous Metals," ASTM Standards Part 2, 745, 748 (1952).

Johnson, J. B. and Hassell, E. J., "Titanium in Aircraft," *Metal Progress,* **60,** 51 (Sept., 1951).

Spretnak, J. W., Fontana, M. G. and Brooks, H. E., "Notched and Unnotched Tensile and Fatigue Properties of Ten Engineering Alloys at 25C and —196C," *Trans. Am. Soc. Metals,* **43,** 547 (1951).

Williams, W. L., "The Titanium Program at the U. S. Naval Experiment Station," *J. Am. Soc. Naval Engineers,* **62,** 833 (1950).

Walden, E. and Dixon, L. A., "Properties and Structure of Titanium after 30 Min Heating at 1200 to 2000° F," *Metal Progress,* 89 (Aug., 1953).

Luster, D. R., Went, W. W. and Kaufmann, D. W., "Creep Properties of Titanium," *Materials & Methods,* 100 (June, 1953).

Kiefer, G. C. and Harple, W. W., "Stress-Corrosion Cracking of Commercially Pure Titanium," *Metal Progress,* 74 (Feb., 1953).

4. PROPERTIES OF COMMERCIAL TITANIUM ALLOYS

The technology of titanium is so new that no industry-wide standard alloys have been developed. However, a few elements are currently receiving major consideration as alloying additions.

Allen has classified the most promising alloys into three groups, (1) those based on chromium and iron which take advantage of the fact that iron is a normal impurity in the sponge; (2) those employing manganese, reported to be more ductile than the others and consequently used for sheet; and (3) those containing aluminum in addition to chromium iron or manganese considered to be superior for elevated temperature service. Recently molybdenum has been added to improve ductility and an iron-vanadium alloy has been developed. The latest addition to the field is an aluminum-tin alloy which is claimed to have superior welding properties.

There are at least ten different alloys on the market at present, each producer having selected compositions which, in his opinion, were best. Briefly, these alloys are characterized by the producers as follows:

Ti-140A is a two-phase alloy sold primarily as bar and forgings, but also in experimental production as sheet and strip. It has good high temperature stability and excellent shock resistance as measured by the impact test.

Ti-150A is an alloy sold primarily as bars and forgings which is moderately responsive to heat treatment.

Ti-155AX is a high strength forging alloy in which the beta phase is stabilized by iron, chromium, and molybdenum and sufficient aluminum is added to retain high strength up to 1000° F. This alloy is still limited to experimental production.

RC-130A is a binary manganese alloy in which the manganese increases the strength of the beta phase without greatly affecting the alpha. The combination yields a high strength alloy with excellent bend ductility.

RC-130B is an aluminum manganese alloy. The addition of aluminum strengthens the alpha but does not greatly affect the beta phase. The alloy is not as ductile as RC-130A but has better hot strength.

A-110AT is the only all-alpha alloy on the market. It has good strength and ductility at room and elevated temperatures. Still in experimental production, it is being tried both as a sheet and as a forging alloy.

MST3Al-5Cr is a high strength forging alloy.

Tensile strengths ranging from 140,000 to 240,000 psi can be obtained. The alloy has high strength at elevated temperatures. It is heat treatable by an isothermal method.

MST2.5Fe-2.5V and MST2Al-2Fe are in process of development as sheet alloys and moderate strength forgings. They are semi-commercial at present.

No information was obtained from Republic Steel on its alloys. However, the compositions indicate that RS-120 is a sheet alloy and RS-110 is a forging alloy.

In addition to these comments made by the producers, certain generalizations on a few of the forging alloys were made by a consumer recently, in an SAE symposium. It was stated that MST3Al-5Cr is the leading forging alloy in tensile, fatigue and elevated temperature tensile strength. Room temperature yield strengths of 160,000 psi are obtainable while ductility runs from 5 to 10 per cent. Yield strengths of 60,000 psi or better were obtained at 800° F.

Of the moderate strength alloys, Ti-150A and RC-130B are strong enough to show a strength/density advantage over competing aircraft materials and are sufficiently ductile to adjust to highly variable stress patterns. RC-130B is less sensitive to directional properties than most of the medium strength alloys and has relatively high strength in the range from 400 to 700° F.

The compositions of the commercial alloys are given in Table 4-1. There does not seem to be any

Table 4-1. Composition of Titanium Alloys

Designation	Producer	C	Nominal Composition—%						
			Al	Cr	Fe	Mn	Mo	Sn	V
Aluminum-Iron Alloy MST2Al-2Fe	Mallory-Sharon	0.5	2	—	2	—	—	—	—
Al-Cr-Fe-Mo Alloy Ti-155AX*	Titanium Metals	0.1 max	5	1.4	1.3	1.4	—	—	—
Aluminum-Manganese Alloy RC-130B	Rem-Cru	0.2 max	4	—	—	4	—	—	—
Aluminum-Tin Alloy* A-110AT	Rem-Cru	—	5	—	—	—	—	2.5	—
Chromium-Aluminum Alloy MST3Al-5Cr	Mallory-Sharon	0.5	3	5	—	—	—	—	—
Chromium-Iron Alloys									
Ti-150A	Titanium Metals	0.02 max	—	2.7	1.5	—	—	—	—
RS-110	Republic Steel	—	—	4	2	—	—	—	—
Cr-Fe-Mo Alloy Ti-140A	Titanium Metals	0.07 max	—	2	2	—	2	—	—
Iron-Vanadium Alloy MST2.5Fe-2.5V	Mallory-Sharon	0.5	—	—	2.5	—	—	—	2.5
Manganese Alloys									
RC-130A	Rem-Cru	0.2 max	—	—	—	7	—	—	—
RS-120	Republic Steel	—	—	—	—	7	—	—	—

* Experimental grade in limited production.

Table 4-2. Physical Properties of Titanium Alloys

Commercial Designation	Density Lb/Cu In.	Melting Range F	Thermal Cond Btu/Hr/Sq Ft/Ft/F at 212° F	Coef of Exp Per F	Specific Heat Btu/Lb/F	Elect Resist Microhm-Cm	Mod of Elasticity Psi
MST2Al-2Fe	0.165	—	—	6.4×10^{-6}	—	120	16,500,000
Ti-155AX	0.163	—	—	—	—	—	15,000,000
RC-130B	0.17	2910-3090	—	—	—	—	16,500,000
A-110AT	0.16	—	—	—	—	—	17,000,000
MST3Al-5Cr	0.166	—	—	6.0×10^{-6}	—	140	16,000,000
Ti-150A	0.166	—	8-10	5.0×10^{-6}	0.129	60	
RS-110	0.17	—	—	—	—	—	
Ti-140A	0.169	—	—	—	—	79	16,500,000
MST2.5Fe-2.5V	0.167	—	—	5.3×10^{-6}	—	80	15,600,000
RC-130A	0.17	2550-2740	—	—	—	—	15,500,000
RS-120	0.17	—	—	—	—	—	

logical method of classification and therefore the alloys are listed in alphabetical order based on the major alloying constituent. All are two-phase alloys excepting A-110AT which is an all-alpha alloy.

Physical Properties

Considerably less information has been reported on the physical properties of the alloys than is available on commercial titanium.

All of the alloys have densities in the range of 0.16 to 0.17 lb/cu in. and thus do not differ greatly from the base material.

Coefficients of expansion appear to be slightly higher than have been reported for titanium, while the single values reported for thermal conductivity and specific heat are the same as those assigned to commercial titanium.

Values of the modulus of elasticity range from 15,000,000 to 17,000,000 psi. For the alloy Ti-150A a modulus of elasticity of 16,400,000 psi, a modulus of rigidity of 6,200,000 psi and a Poisson's ratio of 0.328 have been reported.

The electrical resistivities of the alloys are higher than those of the various grades of commercial titanium ranging from 60 to 140 microhm centimeters.

Mechanical Properties

Typical mechanical properties of eleven commercial alloys are given in Table 4-3. In the annealed condition tensile strength ranges from about 120,000 to 150,000 psi for the duplex alloys

Table 4-3. Mechanical Properties of Titanium Alloys

Commercial Designation	Form	Condition	Yld Str 0.2% Offset Psi	Ten Str Psi	Elong % 2 in.	Red of Area %	Hardness Rockwell	Hardness Brinell
MST2Al-2Fe	Sheet / Forgings	Annealed / Full Hard / Hot Forged[3]	135,000 / 160,000 / 140,000	145,000 / 180,000 / 150,000	12 / 5 / 11	— / — / 30	R_A 66 / R_A 70 / R_A 67	— / —
Ti-155AX	Forgings, hot rolled bars	Annealed	140,000	155,000	12[1]	—	—	300-370
RC-130B	Forgings and bars	Annealed	130,000	140,000	10	—	Rc 34	—
A-110AT	Sheet	Annealed	110,000	116,000	18	40	—	—
MST3Al-5Cr	Forgings	Hot Forged[3]	140,000	150,000	6	20	R_A 71	—
Ti-150A	Plate / Forgings, hot rolled bars	Annealed / Annealed	120,000[2] / 120,000[2]	140,000-165,000 / 135,000-160,000	12[2] / 15[2]	— / —	— / —	311-364 / 311-364
RS-110	—	Annealed	110,000[2]	120,000[2]	12[2]	—	Rc 35	—
Ti-140A	Sheet strip / Plate / Forgings, hot rolled bars	Annealed / Annealed / Annealed	120,000-135,000 / 120,000-135,000 / 120,000[2]	130,000-150,000 / 130,000-150,000 / 130,000[2]	12[2] / 12[2] / 12[2]	— / — / —	Rc 30-34 / — / —	— / 310-350 / 300-340
MST2.5Fe-2.5V	Sheet / Forgings	Annealed / Full Hard / Hot Forged[3]	130,000 / 155,000 / 135,000	140,000 / 175,000 / 145,000	12 / 3 / 9	— / — / 25	R_A 65 / R_A 69 / R_A 66	— / —
RC-130A	Sheet	Annealed	130,000	140,000	12	—	Rc 35	—
RS-120	—	Annealed	120,000[2]	130,000[2]	10[2]	—	Rc 39	—

[1] Elongation in 1D.   [2] Minimum.   [3] Hot Forged 80-85%.

while the all-alpha alloy has a strength of 116,000 psi. The ductility is measured by the elongation ranges from about 10 to 15 per cent for the annealed duplex alloys and 18 per cent for the alpha alloy. Rockwell hardness ranges from R_A 65 to R_C 35.

In the cold worked condition, tensile strengths of 180,000 psi and elongations of 3 to 5 per cent have been reported for the duplex alloys.

For those alloys which are used as forgings, values of tensile strength up to 150,000 psi with elongations of 11 per cent and Rockwell hardness values of R_A 66-71 have been obtained on material hot-forged with a reduction of 80 to 85 per cent.

Heimerl and Hughes investigated the compressive properties of RC-130A and RC-130B. For annealed RC-130A they reported a compressive yield strength (0.2 per cent offset) of 141,000 psi with a modulus of elasticity of 16,200,000 psi. For annealed RC-130B the compressive yield strength was 152,000 psi and the modulus of elasticity, 17,700,000 psi.

Fatigue Properties

The fatigue properties of titanium alloys like those of commercial titanium have been the subject of much controversy. Remarkably high fatigue strength/tensile strength ratios have been reported for polished specimens and equally remarkably low values for notched samples. At present it is impossible to state whether titanium alloys are or are not more notch sensitive than the steels. Indications obtained recently on, presumably, more uniform quality material than was used in the early work, indicate however that titanium alloys and steel are comparable in notch sensitivity. Until the matter is definitely decided, the designer will be on safer ground if he considers the possibilities of notch sensitivity in his calculations.

Hanink investigated the fatigue properties of RC-130B and Ti-150A in the polished and notched conditions. He found a fatigue strength of 55 per cent of the tensile strength for polished samples of RC-130B but the strength dropped to 8 per cent for a sample having a "V" notch with a root radius of 0.005 in. Under the same conditions of testing, Ti-150A had a fatigue strength of 50 per cent when tested unnotched and 6 per cent when tested on a notched sample. This work indicated that the titanium alloys were more notch sensitive than aircraft steels, which when tested under the same conditions gave a notch fatigue strength of about 15 per cent of the tensile strength. However, recent work by Hanink on RC-130B as reported in the Rem-Cru Review gave a value of 14 per cent when using the same root radius as used previously which is within the steel range.

Other recent work on titanium alloys performed at several aircraft companies has been reported also in the Rem-Cru Review. An unnotched endurance limit of 90,000 psi, equal to 59 per cent of the tensile strength was reported for RC-130B. A notched value of 45,000 psi or 26 per cent of the tensile strength was obtained using a notch with a root radius of 0.010 in. Preliminary results of tension-tension testing with the minimum stress ¼ of the maximum stress indicated a fatigue strength of 66 to 79 per cent of the tensile strength for RC-130A.

Finlay, Jaffee, Parcel and Durstein report that preliminary tests on A-110AT indicate that the endurance limit is about 70,000 psi or 58 per cent of the tensile strength.

Bishop, Spretnak and Fontana investigated the properties of RC-130B and Ti-150A at room and sub-zero temperatures. In their room temperature tests, they found a polished fatigue strength of 84,000 psi for RC-130B which is 56 per cent of the tensile strength and a notched fatigue strength (root radius 0.010 in.) of 44,000 psi or 29 per cent of the tensile strength. For Ti-150A they found a polished fatigue strength of 110,000 psi or 76 per cent of the tensile strength while on the notched specimen (root radius 0.010 in.) the value fell to 32 per cent of the tensile strength.

The best ratios for titanium alloys have been reported for polished specimens. Hanink investigated the effects of shot peening on the fatigue strength of SAE 4335 steel and Ti-150A. He found that shot peening the steel raised the endurance limit from the 48 per cent value obtained on polished material to 55 per cent of the tensile strength. In marked contrast, a similar treatment caused a reduction in the ratio from 0.50 to 0.32 for Ti-150A. He concluded that the apparently detrimental effects of this treatment may imply that titanium engine components might be particularly sensitive to nicks or scratches caused in handling or during engine operation.

Corrosion fatigue tests do not seem to have been reported for the alloys and thus it is not possible to indicate whether the excellent fatigue values obtained with commercial titanium are also characteristic of the alloys.

Elevated Temperature Properties

The short time tensile properties of a number of titanium alloys are given in graphs. (Figs. 4-1, 4-2, 4-3, 4-4 and 4-5). The strongest alloy in commercial production at present is MST3Al-5Cr. With this material 0.2 per cent offset yield strengths of about 95,000 psi are obtainable at 800° F which is about the limit of practical operation for these alloys. However, an alloy in experimental production, Ti-155AX, is reported to have a yield strength of 130,000 psi at 800° F and thus promises to be one of the leading alloys for elevated temperature service. These yield strengths compare with 60,000 psi for RC-130A, 75,000 psi for RC-130B and 55,000 psi for Ti-150A at the same temperature. Above 800°F the strengths of all of these materials fall very rapidly.

The ductility as measured by the elongation is less than 20 per cent from room temperature to 800° F for RC-130A, RC-150B and MST3Al-5Cr and between 20 and 30 per cent for Ti-150A over the same range. For all of the alloys there is a sharp increase in elongation above 800° F. Thus at 1000° F, RC-130A has an elongation of 45 per cent,

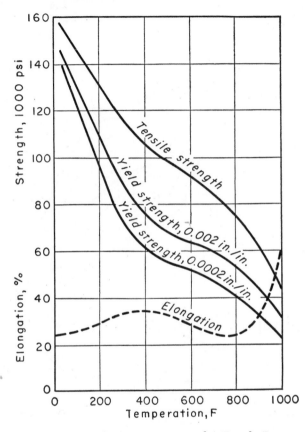

Fig. 4-1. Effect of Temperature on the Tensile Properties of Ti-150A (Titanium Metals)

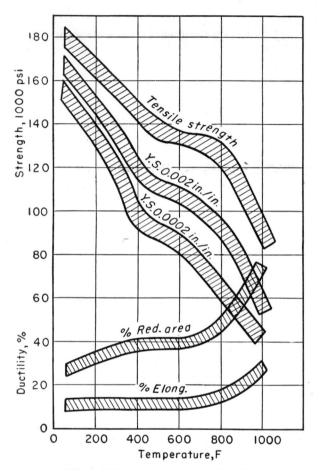

Fig. 4-2. Effect of Temperature on the Tensile Properties of MST3Al-5Cr (Mallory-Sharon) .

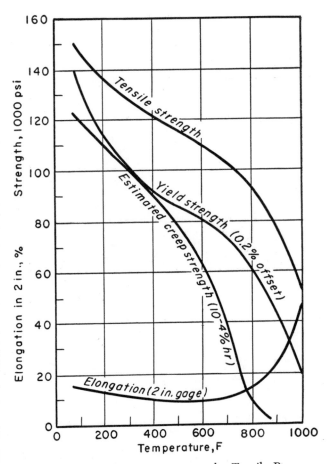

Fig. 4-3. Effect of Temperature on the Tensile Properties of RC-130A (Rem-Cru)

69

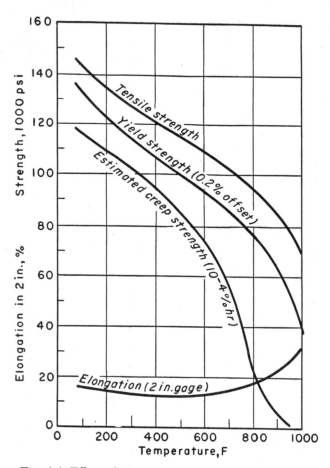

Fig. 4-4. Effect of Temperature on the Tensile Properties of RC-130B (Rem-Cru)

Ti-150A 60 per cent, RC-130B 30 per cent and MST3Al-5Cr about 25 per cent.

The effects of temperature on the elastic constants for Ti-150A have been determined. The modu-

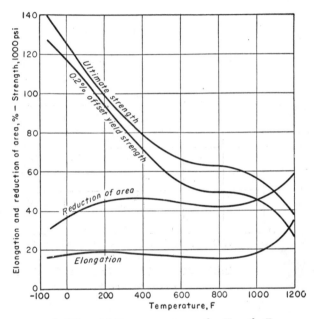

Fig. 4-5. Effect of Temperature on the Tensile Properties of A-110AT (Finlay, Jaffee, Parcel and Durstein)

lus of elasticity falls from 16,400,000 psi at 80° F to 11,600,000 psi at 1000° F, the modulus of rigidity falls from 6,170,000 psi to 4,200,000 psi over the same range and Poisson's ratio increases from 0.328 to 0.386.

71

Heimerl and Hughes investigated the structural efficiencies under short time compression loading of a number of materials at elevated temperatures. Excluding the effects of creep, they found that aluminum alloys 24S-T6 and 75S-T6 were efficient for compression loading applications up to about 300° F. From 300 to 900° F titanium alloys RC-130A

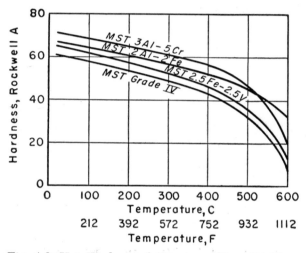

Fig. 4-6. Hot Hardness of Titanium Alloys (Mallory-Sharon)

and RC-130B look promising. At higher temperatures, a good high temperature heat resisting alloy is required to provide a structure having adequate strength and minimum weight.

Fatigue values reported for Ti-150A indicate that this material has a fatigue strength of about 50 per cent of the tensile strength from room temperature to 1000° F. The fatigue strengths of RC-130B were determined on polished and notched specimens at 600° F by one of the aircraft companies and reported in Rem-Cru Review. An endurance limit of 61,000 psi was obtained on unnotched

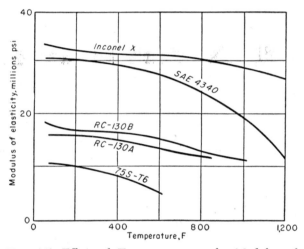

Fig. 4-7. Effect of Temperature on the Modulus of Elasticity (Heimerl and Hughes)

specimens. This value was 53 per cent of the 600° F tensile strength or 40 per cent of the room temperature tensile strength. A notched sample (root radius 0.005 in.) gave a notched fatigue strength at 600° F equal to 19 per cent of the 600° F tensile strength or 15 per cent of the room temperature tensile strength.

Long time properties are more important for applications at elevated temperatures than the short time properties. These are not so fully covered as those for commercial titanium, but values are appearing gradually in the literature.

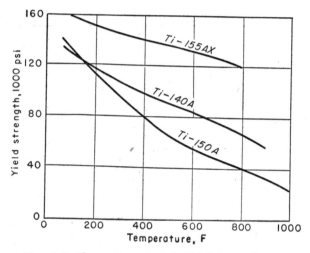

Fig. 4-8. Short Time (1 hr) Yield Strengths at 0.2 percent Offset for Several Titanium Alloys (Titanium Metals)

In stress rupture tests, MST3Al-5Cr is stronger at elevated temperatures than the other commercial alloys on which data have been reported. At 1000° F, MST3Al-5Cr has a 1000 hr rupture strength of 25,000 psi compared with about 8000 psi for Ti-150A. Stress rupture data for Ti-140A are reported to be practically identical with those obtained on Ti-150A. However, the producer emphasizes that Ti-140A does not show significant aging until temperatures rise well above 600° F while Ti-150A must be limited to service below 500° F.

Table 4-4. MAXIMUM TEMPERATURE FOR CREEP OF 0.1%
PER 1000 HR AT 22,400 PSI

(Allen)

Material	Temperature °F
Arc Melted Titanium	under 650
Graphite Melted Titanium	about 650
7% Manganese-Titanium Alloy	nearly 750
4% Manganese-4% Aluminum-Titanium Alloy	about 800
Ferritic creep-resisting steels	850-1025
Simple austenitic steels	925-1225
Special creep-resisting alloys	1475+

Creep determinations indicate that the sustained load carrying abilities of the titanium alloys are quite low at temperatures above 800° F, a result which should be expected from the short time properties. Allen has classified titanium and two of the alloys on the basis of the maximum temperature which will give a creep rate of 0.1 per cent extension in 1000 hr under a load of 22,400 psi. These data are included in Table 4-4 together with similar data for representative steels.

Low Temperature Properties

An extensive investigation of low temperature properties of RC-130B and Ti-150A was reported by

Bishop, Spretnak and Fontana. Their work indicates that the yield and tensile strengths and the hardness of both alloys almost doubles when the temperature falls from ambient to that of liquid nitrogen ($-321°$ F). The ductility, as measured by an impact test, falls sharply. Data appear in Table 4-5.

Table 4-5. Low Temperature Properties
of Titanium Alloys
(Bishop, Spretnak and Fontana)

	RC-130B		Ti-150A	
Temperature F	77	-321	77	-321
Modulus of Elasticity, Psi	16,800,000	18,900,000	15,900,000	19,000,000
Yield Str (0.2% offset) Psi	143,000	254,000	144,000	246,000
Tensile Str Psi	149,000	256,000	153,000	246,000
Elong % (1 in.)	20	2.1	6.5	0.8
Reduction of Area %	41	4.9	9.1	1.6
Fatigue Str (10^7 cycles) Psi	84,000	130,000	110,000	141,000
Vickers Hardness No.	358	602	342	578
Impact Test (Charpy, Keyhole Notch) Ft-lb	10	2.6	12.8	3.0

Tyler, Nesbitt and Wilson also investigated the effects of low temperature on the impact strength of RC-130B. The Charpy impact strength dropped from an average of 15 at room temperature to about 6 at $-321°$ F and remained unchanged when the temperature was reduced to $-423°$ F.

Finlay, Jaffee, Parcel and Durstein showed that the alloy A-110AT increased in tensile strength from 116,000 psi at room temperature to 136,000 psi at −80° F while elongation and reduction of area dropped moderately. Charpy impact values (V-notch) were 20 at room temperature and 16 at −40° F.

Fatigue strengths were determined also by Bishop, Spretnak and Fontana at −108 and −321°

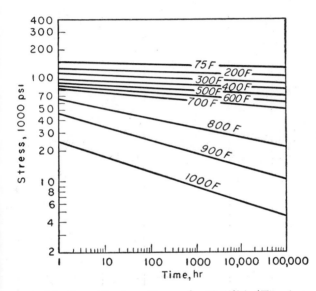

Fig. 4-9. Stress-Rupture Curves for Ti-150A (Titanium Metals)

F on both polished and notched specimens of RC-130B and Ti-150A. A notch having a root radius of 0.010 in. was used. For RC-130B they found a polished fatigue strength of about 57 per cent of the tensile strength at −108° F, while for the notched sample the value was 32 per cent. At −321° F, values were 51 per cent of the tensile strength for the polished sample and 23 per cent for the notched one. For Ti-150A, they found a fatigue strength of 69 per cent of the tensile strength on the polished

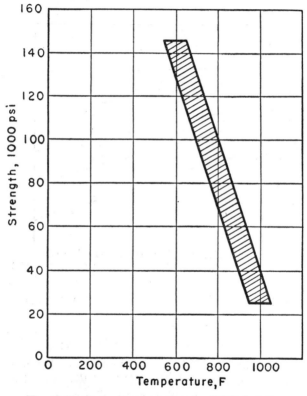

Fig. 4-10. Stress-Rupture Curves (1000 hr) for MST3Al-5Cr (Mallory-Sharon)

material at $-108°$ F with 32 per cent on the notched sample. Values at $-321°$ F were 54 per cent of the tensile strength for the polished sample and 27 per cent for the notched one.

In discussing the results, Dugger stated that the notched fatigue strengths of RC-130B and Ti-150A at $-321°$ F compare favorably with those of 24S-T4 and 75S-T6 aluminum alloys, AZ31 magnesium alloy and a number of structural aircraft steels.

References

Allen, N. P., "The Manufacture and Properties of Titanium and Its Alloys," *Metal Treatment and Drop Forging*, 245 (June, 1953).

Bradford, C. I., Frazier, L. R., Hansen, M., Kessler, H. B., Kostock, F. R. and Williams, W. L., "Titanium Today and Tomorrow," *SAE Journal*, 20 (May, 1953), 56 (June, 1953).

Heimerl, G. L. and Hughes, P. J., "Structural Efficiencies of Various Aluminum, Titanium and Steel Alloys at Elevated Temperatures," *NACA* Technical Note 2975 (July, 1953).

Hanink, H. H., "Applications of Titanium To Aircraft Engines," *SAE Preprint No. 755* (April, 1952).

Anon. "The Fatigue Characteristics of Rem-Cru Titanium and Titanium-Base Alloys, RC-70, RC-130A and RC-130B," *Rem-Cru Titanium Review*, 2 (July, 1953).

Finlay, W. L., Jaffee, R. I., Parcel, R. W. and Durstein, R. C., "Tin Increases Strength of Ti-Al Alloys Without Loss of Fabricability," *Jour. Metals*, 25 (Jan., 1954).

Bishop, S. M., Spretnak, J. W. and Fontana, M. G., "Mechanical Properties, Including Fatigue of Titanium-Base Alloys RC-130B and Ti-150A at Very

Low Temperatures," *Trans. American Society of Metals,* **45,** 993 (1953).

Tyler, W. W., Nesbitt, L. B. and Wilson, Jr., A. C., "Some Low Temperature Properties of Titanium Alloy RC-130B and Stainless Steel," *Journal of Metals,* 1104 (Sept., 1953).

Dugger, E., Discussion, *Trans. American Society of Metals,* **45,** 1006 (1953).

5. HEAT TREATMENT

The heat treatment of titanium is still in the experimental stage with the possible exception of annealing procedures. Consequently, most of the work reported has been on laboratory scale tests. Various theories have been proposed, some of which are quite contradictory. It is possible therefore only to indicate by selecting some examples, the direction in which work in this field is proceeding.

According to Hansen and Kessler, heat treatments suitable for the titanium alloys are basically similar to those employed for ferrous and other nonferrous alloys. Response to heat treatment is the result of the transformation of an unstable high temperature phase at some lower temperature. These researchers list three types of treatment which can occur (1) precipitation of a new phase from supersaturated beta, (2) eutectoidal decomposition of beta into two new phases and (3) transformation to some unstable structure. One or more of these reactions can be used with the heat-treatable titanium alloys. Iron, chromium and manganese are elements which yield diagrams of the iron-iron carbide type. Molybdenum and vanadium are completely soluble in beta titanium and in sufficient quantities stabilize the beta phase to room temperature. Aluminum, oxygen and nitrogen raise the transformation temperature and stabilize alpha titanium.

On the other hand, Jaffee states that quench hardening heat treatments similar to those used for steel are not applicable to the titanium alloys, particularly those with interstitial alloying elements such as carbon. Alloys containing iron, chromium or other beta stabilizing elements offer possibilities but results are poor because the beta phase is retained and causes trouble during tempering. Jaffee further states that age-hardening of unstable beta is possible but excessive brittleness occurs and the aged material is unstable at elevated temperatures. As a result, most alpha-beta alloys, which include practically all of the commercial alloys are used in the fully stabilized condition.

These two statements point out the somewhat uncertain state of knowledge of the underlying principles. The practice is also not very well established.

Annealing

The crystal structure of titanium changes from hexagonal (alpha) the room temperature modification to body-centered cubic (beta) at 1615° F. Slight hardening effects resulting from this change have been reported for quenched commercial titanium but they have no practical significance.

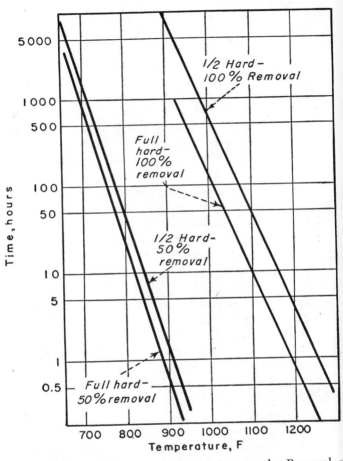

Fig. 5-1. Effects of Time and Temperature on the Removal of Cold Work in RC-70 Titanium Sheet (Rem-Cru)

83

Commercial titanium can be hardened only by cold working and the purpose of heat treating is to soften for further work or to relieve strains. Annealing can be accomplished by heating in the range 1200 to 1300° F for periods of time which depend on the thickness. Strain hardening can be removed by heating in this range for 10 to 15 min. There is a difference of opinion on the effect of the atmosphere in annealing. Some authorities believe that annealing in air is satisfactory for heavy sections but that there is danger of embrittlement if thin sheet, tubing and wire are annealed in air. Inert atmosphere annealing is suggested for thin sections. Others believe that the short time required for annealing thin material at 1200° F makes it possible to anneal in air with no danger of embrittlement. It is generally considered that holding titanium for long periods in the annealing range in air will result in heavy scale formation and the possibility of seriously embrittling the material. Titanium can be stress-relief annealed in the range 600 to 800° F.

Annealing of titanium alloys varies with the composition but the manufacturers generally recommend one hour at 1200 to 1300° F and air cooling. Stress relieving can be achieved generally by heating in air at 750° F.

A problem which is reported frequently is rapid grain growth during heating to high temperatures. It is not possible to refine the grain by any known method of heat treatment although heating for periods of the order of 48 hr in the annealing range will improve ductility somewhat. As an example, the producer states that on heating Ti-150A above 1650° F a coarse grain develops which is difficult to overcome by heat treatment. Extremely slow cooling or reheating in the range 1100 to 1200° F for extended periods of time tends to improve the ductility but the operation is said to be critical.

Table 5-1. RECOMMENDED ANNEALING SCHEDULES
(Titanium Metals)

Material	Temp F	Time hr	Remarks
Ti-75A	1200	½	per inch of thickness
Ti-150A	1200	48	for heavy forgings
Ti-140A and Ti-155AX	1150-1250	2	for forgings, plate and bar
		¼	At temperature for sheet and strip—add 1 hr per inch of thickness to come to temperature

Two methods which have been suggested for refining the grain are, (1) hot working in the range 1200 to 1475° F followed by a short period of heating just above the boundary of the beta-alpha + beta boundary or (2) cold working followed by similar treatment. Although these procedures might serve during the early stages of processing they are hardly applicable for the restoration of finished forgings or similar parts. The best procedure is the avoidance of coarse grain structure by the selection of proper finishing temperatures.

It appears to be generally agreed that the most important factor in titanium alloy fabrication is to keep the grain size as small as possible. This applies to forging, rolling, etc. If the fabricating procedures are so controlled that a fine grain size is obtained, subsequent heat treatment can be beneficial. If a coarse grain size results no thermal treatment can restore the physical properties.

Jaffee recommends stabilizing heat treatments to put the alpha-beta alloys into their softest condition. Such heat treatments involve heating the alloy to a temperature of about 1100 to 1300° F and holding for sufficient time to completely transform the beta phase into massive alpha. A similar result can be achieved by cooling slowly from about 1300 to 1100° F.

Hardening Treatments

Most of the work in this field has been done on experimental alloys and thus procedures applicable to the present commercial alloys have not been reported extensively. Brief comments on a few of these investigations follow.

Worner investigated binary titanium-iron alloys and determined that they are hardenable by quenching and tempering. Water quenching from 1725° F, reheating to 900 to 950° F for a short time and again water quenching almost doubled the tensile strength and hardness and reduced the elongation about 50 per cent.

In an extensive investigation, Duwez found that in binary alloys the beta phase can be retained on quenching if sufficient alloying element is present. The requirements were 12 per cent molybdenum; 15 per cent vanadium; 6 per cent manganese; 4 per cent iron; or 6 per cent chromium.

In certain ternary alloys, Parris, Frost and Jackson found that the beta phase was retained completely on quenching if 7 to 8 per cent of alloying elements were present. Age hardening in these alloys is produced by (1) cooling at a critical rate from a temperature in the alpha-beta or beta region or (2) quenching from this temperature range to retain the beta phase followed by reheating for a suitable period at temperatures above 200° F. Overaging accompanied by softening occurs rapidly at temperatures of 800° F or higher.

Parris, Hirsh and Frost state that certain titanium alloys containing chromium or manganese can be hardened by quenching from 1750° F and aging at 200 to 300° F. The increase in hardness can be as high as 100 Vickers numbers.

Recommendations for the heat treatment of several commercial alloys have appeared however and, no doubt, additional procedures will be reported shortly since there is considerable activity in this field.

Busch states that an isothermal heat treatment has been developed for the alloy MST3Al-5Cr. This treatment consists in heating the alloy at 1750 to 1925° F for 1 hr per inch of cross-section, and without cooling to room temperature transferring the material to a furnace held in the range 950 to 1475° F, the temperature depending on the section size. The heat treatment is reported to give reproducible properties at a predetermined strength level in sections up to 2 in.

Perry states that RS-120 forgings with a cross-section of 1½ in. have been heat treated to 150,000 psi yield strength, 192,000 psi tensile strength with an elongation of 12 per cent by heating for 2 hr at 1300° F, air cooling, reheating to 800° F for 8 hr and again air cooling. He reported also that RS-110 and RS-120 can be age hardened by rapid cooling from 1000° F and reheating to 800° F.

Surface Hardening

When titanium-base materials are heated in air, surface hardening occurs as the result of the absorption of oxygen and nitrogen. Experimental values are shown in Fig. 5-2. These results indicate that selective hardening of the surface is possible by procedures similar to those used for steel. Considerable work has been done in this field and at least one patent, covering hardening by treatment in molten cyanide, has been issued. In common with the other heat treating procedures discussed previously, the investigations have been run on small scale laboratory samples and therefore are merely indicative of the possibilities. Brief comments on some of these investigations will serve to indicate possible future commercial procedures.

Nitriding

Silk investigated the nitriding of titanium and several titanium alloys with ammonia and nitrogen.

For commercial titanium he determined that the optimum conditions were 16 hr at 1600° F in ammonia or 16 hr at 1800° F in nitrogen. He also determined that excessive time periods cause softening of the case. Ti-150A also reached its maximum hardness under similar treatment schedules but could be heated as much as 64 hr without

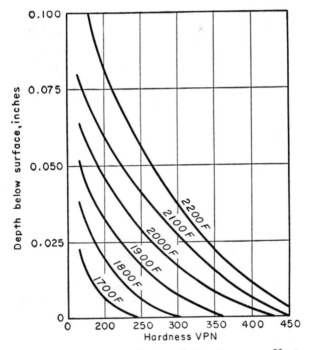

Fig. 5-2. Surface Hardening of Titanium upon Heating for 1 hr in Air at the Temperature Indicated (Titanium Metals)

loss in hardness. The maximum case depth was 0.003 in. in these materials. Nitriding MST3Al-5Cr, MST2.5Fe-2.5V, and MST2Al-2Fe produced moderate increases in hardness. With these materials the maximum case depth reported was 0.022 in.

Wyatt and Grant also investigated the nitriding of commercial titanium with ammonia. They found that there was an optimum treating time for each temperature with greater or lesser time periods giving thinner cases. Temperatures of 1350 to 1700° F yielded similar surface hardness regardless of time of treatment. Comparable cases were produced by using nitrogen instead of ammonia. However, the time required to give equivalent results was 2 to 3 times as long as with ammonia and the temperatures were 200 to 300° F higher.

In decided contrast with these results, it was reported in a symposium held at Armour Institute that a purified nitrogen atmosphere is superior to dissociated ammonia in nitriding titanium and its alloys. Highest hardness values were obtained if a treatment schedule of 16 hr at 1600° F was employed. Longer heating periods produced little change and sometimes resulted in decrease in hardness. Diamond pyramid hardness values of 1000 to 1200 were obtained on Ti-75A, RC-130A, RC-130B and Ti-150A. Case depths averaged about 0.0015 in.

Carburizing

Cases produced by carburizing titanium in a propane-argon atmosphere are reported at the

Armour symposium to have had the best wear characteristics of any hard surfaces produced up to the present time. Recommended conditions are 6 to 8 hr at 1750 to 1800° F in an argon atmosphere containing ½ per cent of propane. Following carburizing, the material is cooled in argon. Shallow cases, 0.0001 to 0.0002 in. deep are produced by this treatment but the hardness is about 1500 on the Knoop scale. The major disadvantage of the treatment is that deeper cases cannot be produced without spalling.

Siliconizing

Siliconized coatings are produced by applying silicon powder and a binder suspended in a low boiling liquid to the surface. After the liquid has been evaporated, the material is heated in an inert atmosphere or a vacuum at a low temperature to remove the binder and then, according to the report made at the Armour symposium, at temperatures of the order of 2600° F. Coatings up to 0.002 in. in thickness are reported. The coatings are reported to protect titanium and its alloys in air up to temperatures of 1800° F. Tests have indicated that a life of 2000 hr can be obtained at 1475° F with siliconized titanium compared with a life of about 100 hr for the unprotected material.

Molybdenizing

Vapor deposition of molybdenum on commercial titanium sheet was reported also in the Armour symposium. Best results were obtained by vacuum treatment, with pressures of 0.5 mm mercury, at a temperature of 1700° F. The coatings were 0.0001 in. in thickness and had a diamond pyramid hardness of 800. These coatings were reported to be sufficiently ductile to withstand a 180 deg bend over a ½ in. radius without failure.

References

Hansen, M. and Kessler, H. D., as reported in "Titanium Today and Tomorrow," Part II Tomorrow, *SAE Journal,* 56 (June, 1953).

Jaffee, R. I., "What the Ferrous Metallurgist Should Know About Titanium," *Iron Age,* 162 (April 2, 1953).

Worner, H. W., "Heat Treatment of Titanium-Rich Titanium-Iron Alloys," *Jour. Institute of Metals,* **80,** 213 (1952).

Duwez, P., "The Martensite Transformation Temperature in Titanium Binary Alloys," *Trans. Amer. Soc. Metals,* **45,** 934 (1953).

Parris, W. M., Frost, P. D. and Jackson, J. H., "Heat Treatment of High Strength Titanium-Base Alloys," *Am. Soc. Metals Preprint 4* (Oct., 1953).

Parris, W. M., Hirsch, L. L. and Frost, P. D., "Low Temperature Aging in Titanium Alloys," *Jour. of Metals,* 178 (Feb., 1953).

Busch, L. S., "Transformation Characteristics of 3 per cent Al-5 per cent Cr Titanium Alloy," *Jour. of Metals,* 146 (Feb., 1953).

Perry, T. E., "Titanium Production and Fabrication at Republic Steel Corp.", *Jour. of Metals,* 150 (Feb., 1953).

Silk, E. J., "Titanium Can be Case-Hardened by Nitriding," *Iron Age,* 166 (Nov. 13, 1952).

Wyatt, J. J. and Grant, N. J., "Nitriding of Titanium

With Ammonia," *Amer. Soc. Metals Preprint 3* (Oct., 1953).

Armour Institute Symposium, "Surface Treatment of Titanium," *Steel*, 130 (Nov. 2, 1953).

6. FORMING AND FABRICATING

The forming of titanium and its alloys has been investigated extensively particularly by the aircraft companies. As a result, considerable information has been developed, especially on the commercially pure material. The forming characteristics of commercial titanium are compared frequently with those of stainless steel. As a matter of fact, it has been stated that any organization which has handled stainless steel will have no difficulties in forming titanium.

However, attempts to fabricate titanium alloys using techniques applicable to steel and the aluminum alloys led to difficulties. When it was recognized that certain modifications in procedure were necessary because alpha titanium has an hexagonal structure, beta has a body-centered cubic structure, and the stronger alloys were combinations of the two, developments in fabricating methods advanced.

A major problem which is still unsolved is the tendency of the metal toward seizing and galling.

This characteristic has hindered the development of fabricating and machining procedures. Practical methods of overcoming galling and seizing are at present limited to the application of coatings or lubricants.

Procedures for the forging of titanium and its alloys and the forming of sheet have been developed to the point where some of them are commercial. In contrast to the work on heat treatment, these operations have been performed on full size equipment. Thus, even experimental work is indicative of the problems which will be encountered in production. Casting is just beginning to approach a stage which shows commercial possibilities. Renewal of interest in the application of powder metallurgy techniques has also been reported.

Table 6-1. PRODUCT SIZE LIMITATIONS

Product	Size Limitation	
	Thickness in.	Width in.
Strip	0.1875 max	24 max
Sheet	0.1875 max	24 min
Plate	0.1875 min	12 min
Bar (other than round)	0.1875 min	12 max
Rod (round section)	0.375 min (dia)	
Wire	0.375 max (dia)	

Reference ASTM Specification B-265

Forging

Forging of titanium is reported to involve no more difficulty than is usually met in working stainless steel. However, Tracy points out that dies used for the production of stainless steel parts are not suitable for producing similar parts from titanium because the latter has less shrinkage than steel. Thus dies should be designed specifically for titanium forging with the shrinkage allowance calculated for this metal. The resistance of titanium alloys to deformation is higher than steel and to forge comparable parts about 25 per cent greater power is required.

Because of the greater force required to cause titanium to flow, dies should be more massive than those used for steel. In their design more generous radii should be employed. Thus, if a steel die is designed with a 7-deg radius, the die to produce a similar part in titanium should have a 10-deg radius. In general, it has been found that the life of dies used for forging titanium is lower than that of dies for producing steel parts.

In almost all closed die forgings there is an opening all around the die impression to permit expulsion of excess material from the die and allow proper closure. Thickness of the flash in steel forging design is determined by the size and shape of the forging. This practice applies also to titanium excepting that experience has shown that for a given part the flash thickness for titanium will be heavier than for steel.

Titanium does not scale in the same manner as steel and the slightest tool mark on the die will be transferred to the forging. In finishing die surfaces, great care is required and usually a final buffing operation is necessary.

Titanium scale is tight and almost invisible. If dies are not kept clean the scale can be driven into the work, resulting in defective forgings. The fact that the scale is invisible and the metal works quite readily at temperatures well below those used for steel leads to a tendency in many forge shops to finish-forge at too high a temperature which can result in greatly reduced ductility in the finished product.

Bar stock must be free from surface cracks or scratches while seams less than 0.002 in. in depth have caused defective forgings which had to be scrapped. For best results in forging titanium moderate reductions should be used.

In general, forging temperatures between 1450 and 1800° F are used in forging both commercial titanium and its alloys. Actual temperatures vary with the size and shape of the part. To minimize surface contamination, the metal should be preheated at 1300° F and quickly heated to the forging temperature with a minimum soaking time. Alloys should be forged at temperatures about 50° F above those used for commercial titanium. For heavy reductions of large sections in open or closed dies, temperatures in the range 1650 to 1800° F should be used. For light reductions, the temperature range can be 1450 to 1550° F and finishing temperatures can be as low as 1300 to 1350° F. If the temperature falls below 1350° F, the metal is sluggish and smooth flow is restricted.

Titanium can be heated in electric, gas or oil-fired furnaces but direct flame impingement must be avoided. Floors should be free from iron scale or the titanium should rest on clean bricks. It has been reported in several instances that titanium bars have reacted with mill scale, the reaction being exothermic and resulting in complete oxidation of the bar.

After forging, it is advisable to anneal the metal at 1200 to 1300° F, holding at temperature for approximately ½ hr per inch of thickness and air cooling.

The preceding remarks indicate some of the problems encountered in forging titanium and its alloys. A number of specific examples have been selected to show the present status of forging development.

Bernstein states that Ti-75A can be forged in the range 1875 to 1400° F. In making small closed die forgings, the blanks were heated to 1850° F and forged between closed impression dies in an 800 lb board drop hammer. The forgings were trimmed and given a light finishing blow. In these tests and in other open die tests, the metal conformed satisfactorily to the die configuration.

Reynolds reported an investigation of the drop forging of Ti-150A. He determined that the alloy could be forged at 1500 to 1750° F, had excellent flow characteristics and gave sharp and clean die forgings. The forgings were made in dies which had been sunk for use with aluminum alloys and no difficulty was experienced with sticking. Both hot and cold removal of flash resulted in clean breaks and the flash-removal characteristics were similar to those of steel.

Coughlin states that the forging of jet engine blades from Ti-150A and RC-130B requires crack-free stock with a maximum hardness of Rockwell C 37. Bar stock is swaged at 950° F, part of the heat being supplied by an induction coil, the balance resulting from the working of the metal. It is necessary to use care to avoid surface folding. Forging dies are designed with large contours to permit free flow of the metal. Dies must be highly polished and lubricated with a mixture of graphite and grease. Upsetting is performed in a press at 1600° F, and blocking on 800 to 2000 lb hammers. After blocking the blades are hot trimmed and tumble blasted to remove scale. Finish forging follows the procedure used in blocking.

Forging titanium alloy compressor wheels has been described by Bullock. These wheels are produced from Ti-150A or RC-130B. Starting material is in the form of 9 in. dia or 9 in. square sections. These are heated to 1750° F and forged directly in the hammer dies. The wheels are 20 to 25 in. in diameter and weigh 80 to 110 lb. Good mechanical properties are obtained with both alloys.

Bullock discussed also the production of smaller forgings ranging from 13 oz to 18 lb in weight using mechanical forging machines, upsetting machines, hydraulic presses and steam drop hammers.

One of these parts was an aircraft piston 6 in. in diameter produced from Ti-150A. The material was heated to 1650° F and pre-blocking was done on a single action hydraulic press. Both blocking and finishing were done on 5000 lb steam drop hammers. In the hammer operations the piece was forged over a plug which formed the inside diameter and wrist pin bosses of the piston. The draft angle on the plug of the blocker die was 5-deg and on the finishing die plug 1 deg.

Forging titanium alloy Ti-150A in a contour die using a slow acting hydraulic press was investigated for the production of a wheel forging 6¾ in. in dia and weighing 13 lb. For comparison similar wheels were made on a drop hammer. The press forgings had higher yield and tensile strengths than the hammer forgings but the ductility was the same for both. Gear forgings were made by hot upsetting in a mechanical upsetting machine with promising results.

Bullock also notes that small shallow die impression forgings can be made with no problems in hammer dies designed for steel, but if the impressions are deep and the draft angles on the male plugs are not greater than 5 deg, trouble with sticking is likely. Forgings made in shallow impressions have smooth surfaces. If there are considerable changes from shallow to deep pockets in the die however, a rough surface often forms on the forging area formed in the deep cavity.

The resistance to deformation of Ti-150A at its forging temperature of 1750° F is greater than that of SAE 4340 at its forging temperature, 2250° F. Compressor wheels were forged in the same equipment from both materials and less blows were required for the steel than for the titanium alloy.

The producer recommends forging MST3Al-5Cr in the range 1825 to 1475° F. To obtain ductile forgings, a finishing temperature of 1475° F should be maintained. Air cooling after forging yields maximum strength and the alloy should not be quenched. For maximum ductility, furnace cooling at a rate not exceeding 300° F per hour is recommended.

One of the large custom forging organizations modifies these suggestions somewhat. Ingots of MST3Al-5Cr are preheated at 1500° F for forging, the temperature is then raised to 1700 to 1750° F for the shortest possible period to achieve through heating. This avoids excessive grain growth which is detrimental to the properties. Upsetting is performed with light blows and is continued until the temperature drops to 1450° F. There is danger of cracking if forging is continued below this temperature. Therefore the forging is reheated, as rapidly as possible to 1750° F and forging is continued. The mechanical properties are higher, the lower the finishing temperature. Completed forgings are sometimes air cooled but many customers specify slower cooling to avoid possible thermal stresses. This cooling is accomplished by burying the forging in limestone or cooling in a furnace.

Cold and Hot Heading

Development of commercial titanium and titanium alloy fasteners has been in progress for several years. Cold heading can be used for the forming of small screws and rivets of the commercial grades. Round head machine screws, ¼-28 by 1⅛ were produced from RC-70. Round head rivets ⅛ by 1 were also cold headed from this material. Ti-75A was used to produce 1/16 by ⅜, 100 deg countersunk rivets at a heading rate of 9500 pieces per hr. The wire was copper plated and in addition drawcote and white lead were used for lubrication. Attempts to cold head RC-130B and Ti-150A were unsuccessful.

For best performance bolts should be stress relieved after heading and before roll threading. Stress relief temperatures between 700 and 1000° F are suggested.

Commercial titanium and alloys were headed also by hot forging. All materials were induction heated prior to forging. Hexagon head bolts ¾-16 by 2½ were produced from RC-70 while socket head cap screws, ½-20 by 3½ were produced from RC-130B. Heating time for the commercial material was 16 sec and for the alloy grade 34 sec. Forging was done at 1625 to 1650° F and the operations included upsetting and piercing.

Forming

Commercial titanium can be formed by bending, stretch-forming, drawing, spinning and similar operations. The formability of annealed sheet has been compared with that of ¼ to ½ hard 18-8 stainless steel. Since the alloys are somewhat stiffer, the formability of alloy sheet in the annealed condition has been compared with ¾ hard 18-8 stainless.

Cold forming should be used if possible. To cold-form titanium higher pressures are required than are necessary for low carbon steels and lower press speeds are desirable. Because of the high rate of work hardening, annealing is required when fabrication calls for repetitive severe straining. Stress-relieving is necessary after forming to prevent cracking.

Bending. Annealed commercial titanium sheet up to 0.095 in. thick can be bent cold 180 deg over a radius of ½T if bends are made parallel to the rolling direction. If the bends are made across the sheet, the radius must be increased to ¾T. In the aircraft industry, however, to compensate for variations in the sheet, bend radii have been 3 to 5T. The great increase in radius has been employed because the quality of titanium sheet has not been equal to that of the stainless steels and aluminum alloys. However, sheet quality is improving as larger and more uniform ingots are coming into production and rolling experience increases and it is probable that the minimum bend radii will be reduced in the near future.

Bending ½ hard commercial titanium sheet can be done over a radius of about 5T although again several aircraft organizations double this figure for room temperature bending. Spring back characteristics are similar to those of stainless steel. To reduce the bending radius to 5T, the material can be heated to 500 or 600° F before bending. Various methods of heating can be used.

To bend RC-70 in the forming of ammunition boxes, one company has developed a method of heating the material electrically. Electrical contacts are fastened directly to the sheet, the high resistance of titanium producing the necessary heating to permit bending. Heating is done in the forming press and continued during the forming operation.

An aircraft company has noted that one of the worst problems encountered in forming sheet was non-uniformity from side to side, that is, the stock bends very well from one surface but fails when bent from the other. This is attributed to the fact that one side of the sheet has absorbed more oxygen and nitrogen during the rolling operations.

To overcome this variation, Baldwin suggests that the bending properties of titanium strip can be improved by removing a thin surface layer, by pickling in a mixture of nitric and hydrofluoric acid. He cites an example of a strip which cracked after a 15 deg bend in the "as received" condition. Following the pickling treatment, the material could be bent satisfactorily through 120 deg.

Deep Drawing. Annealed commercial titanium has been reported to have deep drawing properties similar to those of 24S-0 aluminum but somewhat inferior to those of the stainless steels. According to another report, the permissible reduction of area during deep drawing of commercial titanium and type 302 stainless steel are equal. A third report states that any part which can be deep-drawn using mild steel can be duplicated with commercial titanium.

In deep drawing, press speeds should be lower than those used for steel. More frequent annealing is required and ample punch and die radii are necessary. A draw radius of 8T has been recommended. Pick-up and galling are serious problems and the draw-ring may require frequent cleaning to avoid failures caused by sticking.

Development of suitable lubricants is in progress.

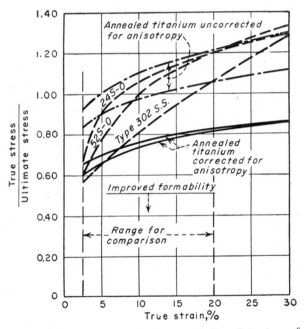

Fig. 6-1. Deep Drawing Farmability Criterion of Commercial Titanium compared with Other Materials (Schroeder)

A proprietary method of coating the surface with solid film lubricants composed of graphite and resins is said to prevent galling and seizing. The use of sulfurized or chloridized polar lubricants has also been suggested. Selective surface oxidation, phosphate coating or copper plating have also been used to reduce seizing.

Less work has been done on alloy sheet than on the commercially pure material. Suggestions have been made that such forming can be done most expeditiously by following the procedures used for magnesium and the stronger aluminum alloys, that is, by heating the sheet for forming.

Gulliksen has established a procedure for the deep drawing of commercial titanium down to at least 0.025 in. gage. He notes that reductions of approximately 40 per cent can be made in conventional deep drawing operations. Because of work hardening however, frequent anneals are required, often after each operation. Stress relieving at 1325° F for 4 to 10 min restores sufficient ductility for additional draws. Since this annealing is done in air, there is a problem of removing the scale formed. This scale must be removed to restore the surface conditions best suited for deep drawing. For this purpose one of the proprietary caustic baths is used.

Gulliksen notes that the biggest problem in deep drawing is the tendency to score or gall. Bonderizing followed by the application of a dry film lubricant on the treated surface, or copper plating have both been used to improve the drawing qualities.

However, frequent polishing of the dies is necessary. Most successful results were obtained by using speeds about ½ those used for mild steel, while draw pressures were greater than for mild steel and comparable to those required in drawing stainless steel.

Hydropress Forming. Reports on hydropress forming indicate that some parts have been formed satisfactorily at room temperature, others have cracked when formed at room temperature but could be formed at elevated temperatures.

For example, titanium alloy frame sections which cannot be made successfully at room temperature on a hydropress, have been produced successfully by heating both press and sheet. The forming blocks were heated to 900° F, the cold blank was placed on the block and heated with a torch. Then blank and die were covered with asbestos insulating fiber, a hard rubber pad was placed over the asbestos and the part was formed in the hydropress.

Spring-back is not completely eliminated even if parts are heated for forming. Two parts of a stiffener lower cowl were formed on a hydropress from 0.025 in. gage commercial titanium sheet. The upper part formed at 550° F had a 5 deg spring-back while the lower part formed at room temperature had a 10 deg spring-back.

Stretch Forming. Titanium stretches easily but does not shrink readily. To prevent buckling of the reduced area, the part can be hot formed or working can be modified so that more stretching and less shrinkage occurs.

107

Stretch forming is one of the most successful methods of fabricating titanium and its alloys. It is difficult to produce shallow draws without spring-back and stretch forming can overcome this problem. If the dies are properly designed spring-back can be almost completely eliminated. The stretch press is reported to be most successful when sufficient stretch can be given to the outside flange of the part to move the neutral axis as close to the inside flange as possible, thus making the compression bend small. The chief limitation is the width of the web. If it is too wide the outside flange would have to be stretched beyond its ability to deform and fracture would result.

Titanium and its alloys can be cold-stretched if slow uniform cycles are used and the maximum extension is about 20 to 30 per cent. Spring-back of commercial titanium is comparable to that of half hard stainless steel but the alloys have greater spring-back in general.

Drop Hammer Forming. Titanium and its alloys can be formed on drop hammers but heating is necessary to avoid fracture. To form a part from titanium requires more operations than would be necessary to form Type 347 steel to the same shape. Hard-faced Kirksite dies with steel inserts are used because ordinary Kirksite dies may be damaged by the heating required.

Power Brake Forming. Forming of commercial titanium was accomplished successfully by heating the die holder, electrically, to a temperature of 500 to 520° F. Parts were preheated in an oven to 875° F before each bend and bending was discontinued when the temperature had fallen to 600° F. Bend radii of the order of 3½T were used in these operations.

In forming titanium on power brakes, operations are reported to be similar to those used for half hard stainless steel. The minimum bend radius should be 3T.

Punch Press Forming. Parts can be cold formed on a punch press but excessive spring-back makes die design difficult. This spring-back may be as high as 7 to 14 deg.

Spinning. Commercial titanium sheet can be spun successfully at elevated temperatures. Certain modifications of the normal spinning procedure are suggested by Rose. The wooden chuck for hand spinning must be protected and this has been done successfully by the use of an aluminum and a steel heat shield. The optimum temperature is 1000 to 1300° F and continuous localized heating is required. Because of the seizing properties of titanium, the usual bronze spinning tools must be replaced with hardened steel rollers. In mechanical shear spinning, the operation is completed so rapidly (in about 40 sec) that preheating the blank to 1300° F in an oven is satisfactory.

Dimpling. High pressure is required to dimple sheet for flush-head riveting. In some sizes the operation can be done at room temperature but for the larger diameter rivets or for work-hardened material, heating the sheet is required to prevent cracking. Temperatures in the range 500 to 600° F are satisfactory.

Shearing. Annealed titanium alloys can be sheared on power shears equipped for processing stainless and other alloy steels. Edges produced are clean and square. Power requirements are similar to those required in shearing ¼ hard stainless steel. Irregular outlines are produced on rotary or nibbler type shears with results comparable to those obtained with ¼ hard stainless steel.

Flaring. Commercial titanium tubing from ½ to ¾ in. in diameter can be bent at room temperature on a mandrel-type tube bending machine using bend radii corresponding to those employed in bending annealed stainless steel tubing. Flaring of the larger sizes has been performed successfully but localized cracks occurred in the flares made on the smaller diameters mentioned. It is difficult to obtain more than 35 per cent increase in diameter in flaring at room temperature. Somewhat greater diameters can be obtained by flaring at temperatures in the range 400 to 600° F.

Casting

The casting of titanium is difficult because the metal is extremely reactive in the molten condition, not only with gases but also with all of the usual refractory materials. However, considerable attention has been devoted to this problem and procedures are being developed which indicate that fabricating by this method may soon be practical.

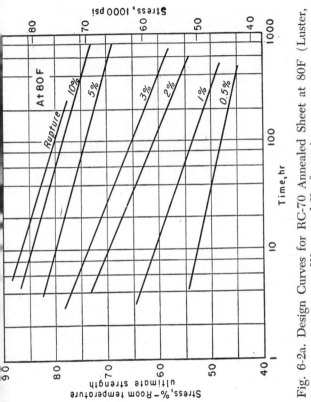

Fig. 6-2a. Design Curves for RC-70 Annealed Sheet at 80F (Luster, Wentz and Kaufmann)

111

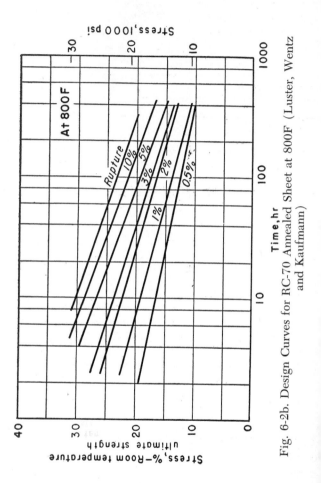

Fig. 6-2b. Design Curves for RC-70 Annealed Sheet at 800F (Luster, Wentz and Kaufmann)

Simmons and McCurdy have developed an arc furnace in which melting and casting are carried out in a gas-tight copper box. Heat is introduced by means of a direct current arc between a water-cooled tungsten electrode and titanium. The charge consists of a slug of titanium, which in their experimental furnace weighs about 12 lb. The arc melts a pool of metal weighing about 3 lb and the unmelted skull of titanium serves as a crucible to hold

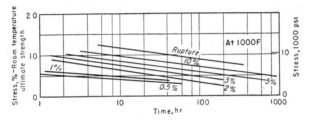

Fig. 6-2c. Design Curves RC-70 Annealed Sheet at 1000F (Luster, Wentz and Kaufmann)

the molten metal, thus preventing contamination of the melt. Purified argon stabilizes the arc and prevents contamination from the atmosphere. The casting is formed by tilting the furnace and allowing the molten metal to run into a mold of machined graphite. This furnace has been used for the production of various titanium alloys weighing up to about 1½ lb on an experimental basis.

Kuhn has also developed an arc furnace for melting titanium which incorporates the furnace and mold in one piece of apparatus. Titanium or titanium alloys are melted in a water cooled copper vessel using an arc current of about 600 to 800 amp. In from 1½ to 2 min the metal is ready to cast, the furnace is tilted and the molten metal flows through the sprue into the mold which is either copper or graphite. Because of rapid cooling, small castings can be removed about 5 min after casting. The apparatus is adaptable either to vacuum or pressure casting, the latter having been used to produce long rods of very small diameter.

The process has been used to produce rods as small as ⅛ in. in diameter, up to 7 in. long. It has also been used to produce small precision castings using investment mold materials. The author states that the process could be adapted to the production of compressor blading for turbine engines in permanent copper molds.

It has been announced recently that titanium alloy castings of complex shapes weighing up to several pounds have been produced in pilot plant quantities by vacuum melting. It was stated that the castings were produced in a vacuum arc furnace using a special molding material which withstands attack by molten titanium. The surface of these castings is said to be equal to that produced on a good sand casting with conventional metals.

It has also been reported that a titanium aircraft latch has been successfully poured experimentally using the frozen mercury process. A regular Mercast mold, developed for casting 1020 steel was used, together with a special ceramic shell. This work is said to indicate a possible solution to the problem of the reaction between molten titanium and investment materials.

Powder Metallurgy

The first methods employed in attempting to fabricate titanium were based on the procedures used in powder metallurgy. However, these were discarded when methods for casting billets were developed.

The advantages of the metal powder process for producing specialized parts have led to a revival of interest in this process and several organizations are engaged in developing procedures.

Starting with titanium sponge, various titanium shapes having controlled porosity and densities varying from 50 to 99.8 per cent of the theoretical value have been produced.

Mechanical tests on parts produced from sponge containing 99.85 per cent titanium have had tensile strengths of 48,000 psi with elongations of 33 per cent and Rockwell hardness values of B65 to 70. Sponge of lower purity has yielded parts having tensile strengths of 65,000 to 85,000 psi and elongation of 15 to 25 per cent.

Among parts which have been produced is a titanium filter having 35 to 50 per cent porosity capable of filtering red and white nitric acid. Excellent corrosion resistance has been reported in this application. The weight loss after 700 hr immersion in fuming nitric at 160° F was less than 0.5 per cent as contrasted with complete dissolution in 168 hr of materials previously used.

Hamajian and Darmara have developed a new powder metallurgy process, details of which have not been announced, which is said to be suitable for the production of shapes having difficult contours. This process is said to produce parts of uniform density even on portions such as undercuts or threads which are usually difficult to press. The parts have uniform hardness and strength throughout their shape and meet tolerances of 0.008 in. Surface finish of the completed component depends on the particle size of the powder. Among parts which have been produced on an experimental basis are a chuck wrench, a turbine blade and a rifle trigger.

References

Tracy, G. S., "Forging of Titanium Requires Special Techniques," *Machinery,* 202 (June, 1953).

Bernstein, H., Private Communication.

Reynolds, T., "Forgings and Drop Forgings in Ti-Alloy 150A," *Light Metals,* 91 (March, 1953).

Coughlin, V. L., "How GE Works Titanium," *American Machinist,* 176 (Feb. 16, 1953).

Bullock, R. J., "Forgings of Titanium," *Proc. Titanium Symposium,* Watertown Arsenal, 10 (Oct. 8, 1952).

Nelson, J. F., "Flat-Die Forging of Cast Titanium Ingots," *Machinery,* 164 (Oct., 1953).

Brenner, H. S., "Titanium Fastener Development Report," *Fasteners,* 9, 7 (Nov. 2, 1953).

Baldwin, Jr., W. N., "How to Improve Bending Properties of Titanium Strip," *Iron Age,* 165 (Dec. 3, 1953).

Guilliksen, J. W., "Cold Forming of Titanium," *Proc. Titanium Symposium,* Watertown Arsenal, 14 (Oct. 8, 1952).

Bradford, C. I., Frazier, L. R., Hansen, M., Kessler, H. D., Kostock, F. R. and Williams, W. L., "Titanium Today and Tomorrow," *SAE Journal*, 20 (May, 1953).

Rose, A. S., "Hot Spinning Improves Workability of Titanium," *Iron Age*, 119 (Feb. 19, 1953).

Wheelon, O. A., "Design and Manufacturing Techniques With Titanium," *SAE Preprint No.* **656** (Oct., 1951).

Fairbairn, G. A., "Working Titanium at North American," *Machinery*, 183 (July, 1953).

Sweet, J. W., "Application of Titanium Sheet-Strip Limited by Presently Available Alloys," *Jour. of Metals*, 143 (Feb., 1953).

Simmons, O. W. and McCurdy, H. R., "Arc Furnace Developed for Casting Titanium," *Amer. Foundrymen's Society Preprint* **53-47** (May, 1953).

Hamjian, H. J. and Darmara, F. N., "New Process Gives Unusual Powder Parts," *Iron Age*, 98 (July 30, 1953).

Kuhn, W. E., "Titanium and Zirconium Castings Now Practicable," *Materials & Methods*, 94 (Dec., 1952).

Luster, D. E., Wentz, W. W. and Kaufmann, D. W., "Creep Properties of Titanium," *Materials & Methods*, 100 (June, 1953).

Schroeder, W., Lockheed Aircraft Corp, private communication.

7. JOINING

Joining titanium and its alloys is one of the more difficult problems facing the fabricator of titanium equipment. However satisfactory procedures are gradually being developed.

Ductile joints in commercial titanium can be obtained by resistance or inert-gas shielded arc welding processes. Good results have been obtained also by brazing and adhesive bonding. Greater difficulties have been encountered with the alloys and at present, flash-butt welding appears to be the most satisfactory welding process.

Some success has been achieved in brazing and adhesive bonding of titanium to dissimilar metals while soft soldering by special techniques has also been reported. The welding of titanium to other metals however has resulted in the formation of extremely brittle joints.

Mechanical joints using titanium or titanium alloy fasteners have been improved by the development of suitable methods of preventing or reducing seizure and galling. Satisfactory riveting procedures using commercial titanium rivets have also been developed.

Effect of Composition on Welding

Holt, Vandenburgh and McClymonds investigated the effect of carbon content in the range 0.1 to 0.6 per cent carbon on the characteristics of spot welded sheet. Based on weld strength, spot welding

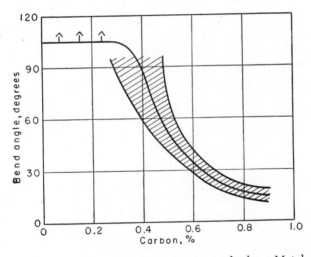

Fig. 7-1. Effect of Carbon content in the base Metal on the bend ductility of Inert Gas Tungsten Arc Welded Titanium Strip. Bend radius 1,5 to 3T. Arrows indicate no fracture. (Mahla and Hitchcock)

conditions for the best results using single-phase a.c. welding equipment of standard design were: welding current 10,000 amps, welding force 1350 lb, time 18 cycles and electrode contour 3 in. radius. There was no significant difference in weld strength over the range of carbon investigated but weld ductility was adversely affected by increasing carbon. Welds in the low carbon grade yielded ductile fractures while those in the 0.6 per cent carbon grade gave brittle fractures.

Mahla and Hitchcock investigated the effect of carbon on the ductility of titanium-carbon welds made by the inert-gas shielded tungsten arc method with an argon atmosphere. The material was commercial grade sheet selected to give a variety of carbon contents ranging from 0.015 to 1.07 per cent. They concluded that increase in carbon content causes decreasing tensile and bend ductility in as-welded material. If ductile bends are required, the carbon content must be limited to 0.24 per cent. They found also that short-time post welding anneals did not improve the ductility of the welds.

Martin investigated the effects of carbon, oxygen and nitrogen on spot and inert-gas shielded tungsten arc welds on titanium sheet. He concluded that in titanium-carbon alloys, good welds were obtained with carbon contents up to 0.13 per cent; between 0.13 and 0.28 per cent carbon, the carbon begins to affect the ductility of both arc and spot welds adversely; and at 0.55 per cent carbon, the ductility of arc welds is practically zero. He determined also that arc welds in titanium containing more than 0.15 per cent oxygen or more than 0.13 per cent nitrogen had low ductility while material containing 0.24 per cent nitrogen was brittle. Spot

120

welding tests gave similar results. On the basis of this work, he suggests that to avoid brittle welds, carbon should be held below 0.28 per cent, oxygen below 0.15 per cent and nitrogen based on incomplete data below about 0.05 per cent.

Faulkner, Grable and Voldrich investigated the effects of iron, manganese, chromium and molybdenum on the properties of welded joints. The work was confined to a study of binary alloys, most of which were in the composition range in which the most promising alloys are found. Inert-gas shielded tungsten arc welded joints of several thicknesses of plate were prepared. The bend ductility of welded joints of low alloy content was fairly good but the ductility decreased rapidly to extremely low values when the alloy content exceeded 3 per cent. Post weld heat treatment improved the ductility of alloys containing up to 6 per cent of the addition element to some extent. Notch toughness tests gave results similar to the bend tests.

Arc Welding. Because of the affinity of titanium for oxygen and nitrogen, only the inert gas shielded processes are suitable for the arc welding of this material and certain conditions must be met if a strong, sound and ductile weld is to be produced. The material must be ductile and of such a composition that weld brittleness will not occur. At present this condition is met only by the commercial grades of titanium in which carbon is lower than about 0.25 per cent and by the titanium-aluminum-tin alloy, A-110AT. All other alloys commercially available are embrittled to some degree by welding.

121

The surfaces to be welded must be clean and free from heavy scale such as that formed during previous hot working. Such scale can be removed by sand blasting followed by hydride descaling and possibly by a dip into a nitric-hydrofluoric acid solution. Some organizations believe that light oxide films do not interfere with welding, others remove these films by a dip into a hydrofluoric or nitric-hydrofluoric acid mixture.

The molten metal in the weld and the hot metal adjacent to it must be fully shielded by a blanket of inert gas.

Barrett, Lane and Huber note that the inert gas coverage must be much greater than it is when welding the less reactive metals. Shielding on both sides of the weld is required and a trailing shield behind the torch is necessary to provide coverage for that part of the weld which has solidified but is still at high temperatures. Others have suggested that protection of the metal is required until the temperature has fallen to 400° F.

Shielding gas which can be argon, helium or a mixture must be practically free from contamination by oxygen, nitrogen and carbon-bearing gases. Barrett, Lane and Huber determined during an investigation of the welding of commercial titanium sheet and wire that an arc weld made in an atmosphere of pure helium has properties comparable to those of the parent metal. Helium atmospheres must contain considerably below 1 per cent of oxygen or nitrogen if the properties of the welded metal are not to be adversely affected. Severe embrittlement occurs if the oxygen or nitrogen content rises to 10 per cent. Hydrogen does not have so great an effect and 10 per cent can be present without affecting the properties of the welds.

The best results with a tungsten electrode are obtained with direct current and a negative electrode polarity, with consumable electrodes, direct current should be used with positive electrode polarity.

These general remarks apply to all arc welding procedures for joining titanium. Comments on the welding of some specific materials follow.

Satisfactory welds on commercial titanium have been made by the inert gas shielded arc process on material from 1/16 in. to ⅛ in. thick with no special preparation of the joint. Plates ½ in. thick have been welded using a 70 deg notch. Adequate gas shielding is extremely important. Welds have been backed both with metal and gas with good results. For welding thin strip, the use of a copper backing strip is advantageous since it provides protection to the under side of the sheet and also holds the material in proper alignment. If welds are not backed, they must be protected with an auxiliary flow of gas. Sound welds have been obtained using argon or helium as shielding gas, tungsten or consumable electrodes (carbon is not recommended because of possible pick-up in the metal) and direct current straight polarity power. Although alternating current can be used the arc tends to wander.

Nippes, Gerken and Schaaf employed the inert-gas shielded consumable-electrode arc process to

123

DONALD E. HENDRIX

investigate the welding of Ti-75A plate. Impact tests showed that the weld metal was much less ductile than either the heat-affected zone or the base metal. However, a heat treatment at 1200° F for 24 hr greatly improved the impact strength of the weld metal. The improvement in properties was attributed to a combination of stress-relief and homogenization.

Begeman, Block and McBee note that Ti-100A can be readily spot welded using a wide range of conditions. Weld penetration is greater and more difficult to control than in most metals. The best results are obtained with low welding time and moderate welding current. They found no significant increase in the hardness of the weld over that of the base metal.

Finlay, Jaffee, Parcel and Durstein studied the weldability of the all-alpha alloy A-110AT by inert-gas shielded arc welding with an atmosphere of helium. Butt welds were made which had bend ductilities equal to those of the parent metal both across and with the grain. Both weld and parent metal also had similar tensile strength and elongation values. They remark that these results were obtained with no post heat treatment. Thus this alloy has properties which resemble those of commercial titanium more nearly than those of the other alloys now in commercial production.

Rosenberg, Hutchinson and Weiss investigated the inert gas arc welding of RC-130A. Welds with excellent appearance were obtained readily but they were so brittle that fracture occurred with practically no bending. Slow cooling from 1500° F in argon improved the bend ductility to the extent that it was possible to make transverse bends of 52 deg and longitudinal bends of 65 deg on the welded material.

In general, Rosenberg notes that for RC-55 and Ti-75A, tensile and bend properties of inert gas shielded arc welded joints are equal to those of the parent metal. For RC-70 and Ti-100A there is a drop in bend ductility of about 50 per cent although the tensile properties are similar to those of the parent metal. With RC-130A, the appearance of the welds is excellent but they were extremely brittle.

Resistance Welding. Spot, seam and flash-butt welding of commercial titanium can be accomplished readily. Some organizations state that welding is similar to that of stainless steel, others compare it with aluminum. Flash-butt welding has also been used for the joining of titanium alloys.

Spot and Seam Welding. The spot welding of commercial titanium sheet offers no particular problem and satisfactory welds can be made over a wide range of conditions. The weld time in cycles is about the same as that required for carbon steel of the same thickness but the welding current is approximately 50 per cent greater. From 25 to 50 per cent more pressure on the electrodes is suggested also.

For spot welding some organizations clean the surfaces to be welded with a degreasing solvent and follow with a nitric-hydrofluoric or a hydrofluoric acid dip. This treatment is reported to reduce the surface contact resistance to a low value.

One of the characteristics which have been reported for titanium is excessive penetration. Since the welds are, in general, somewhat less ductile than the parent metal, conditions should be adjusted by trial to limit the penetration.

Begeman, Block and McBee showed that commercial titanium can be spot welded readily and the resulting weld has high strength and moderate ductility. Tension-shear ratios of 0.35 were obtained. These were similar to ratios obtained with 24ST aluminum and with SAE 1035 steel which had been tempered after spot welding. Weld hardness is only moderately affected by varying the welding current or time and hardness tests indicate that there is not sufficient difference between the hardness of the parent metal and the weld metal to cause embrittlement.

Some fabricators of airframes state also that commercial titanium spot welds have a tensile/shear ratio of 0.32 which is well above the 0.25 minimum required. They suggest that this material is easier to spot weld than aluminum. Another company reports that titanium easily meets the weld quality requirement established for stainless steel sheet.

Clean and scale free commercial titanium can be seam welded with less force than is required in the welding of the same thickness of stainless steel.

The alloy grades of titanium can also be spot welded. Strengths are similar to those obtained on spot welded joints of other metals of equal thickness but the ductility is lower.

Flash Butt Welding. Flash butt welding techniques for titanium resemble those for aluminum alloys more nearly than those for steel. A relatively short flashing cycle is desirable, during which the butted ends are heated to fusion in the arc. A rapid forging cycle follows. Upset pressures are higher and current densities are lower for titanium than they are for aluminum although standard total losses, upset flash and voltage settings can be used.

To produce satisfactory welds, the oxide scale formed during annealing must be removed by methods such as those discussed in the chapter on Cleaning and Finishing. Spot welding does not seem to be affected by the thin oxide coating which forms on titanium at room temperature but for flash butt welding the contact area must be cleaned.

Flash butt welding of titanium can be performed most readily on machines which incorporate rapid push-up and burn-off. This prevents excessive oxidation. Satisfactory weld ductility has been obtained by welding with no protective atmosphere but greater ductility is achieved by shielding with argon. In general, the ductility resulting from flash-butt welding is better than that obtained in inert-gas shielded arc welding because the forging action assists in breaking up the cast structure. To flash butt weld titanium requires about three times the current and about half the time used for steel, and a chamfer angle of 45 deg instead of the 30 deg used for steel welding.

Flash butt welding of Ti-75A produces weld strengths equal to those of the parent metal. Annealing after welding has no appreciable effect on the properties of welds in this material.

Oehler states that titanium alloys can be readily flash butt welded if the material is of good quality and has a uniform structure. Techniques similar to those used for aluminum are employed and welded parts are annealed immediately after completion of the weld. Welds made in RC-130B have had tensile strengths of 152,000 psi, elongations of 15 per cent in 2 in. and reductions of area of 46 per cent.

Cold Welding. Hughes shows that joints can be made by cold pressure welding between titanium and copper, aluminum or iron. On an experimental basis he determined that the deformation required to produce high-strength joints was of the order of 80 per cent and was in the same range as that required for cold welds in copper. This deformation is considerably higher than that required for aluminum.

Following the laboratory tests Hughes cold welded a titanium stud to an aluminum rod and faced a copper x-ray target with titanium by the process. As a result he states that the deformation required for successful joints is sufficiently low to permit use of the process in the fabrication of titanium components.

Brazing

Smith and Yerkovich state that titanium can be brazed by the common commercial methods if proper fluxes are used and the surface is protected from the atmosphere. However, the available commercial fluxes limit the selection of brazing alloys to those melting between 1100 and 1450° F. Compounds are formed with both silver-base and aluminum-base brazing alloys which are apparently brittle. The compounds lead to erratic results in single lap joints but are not so detrimental in double lap joints which are subjected mainly to shearing stresses.

Rapid heating restricts compound formation and leads to more consistant joints than are obtained with torch and furnace brazing techniques. The salt bath brazing of titanium is satisfactory for small objects but is less satisfactory when a large fixture must be heated.

Investigation of the hardness of the joint made in Ti-75A with a typical silver solder gave the following hardness values: titanium base metal 345 Knoop hardness value, intermediate compound 666 Knoop and silver brazing alloy 147 Knoop. This hard brittle interface which is formed with the silver brazing alloys affects joint strength adversely. A similar effect is found when brazing with aluminum alloys.

Meredith reports that induction brazing of commercial titanium in an inert atmosphere with pure silver gave excellent results. Silver has good wetting properties, the alloying effect is negligible and good joint strengths are obtained.

He reports also that commercial titanium can be induction brazed in an inert atmosphere to most of the common steels and non-ferrous alloys. The titanium must be clean, the recommended procedure being vapor blasting of the joint area. However, dipping in a mixture of nitric and hydrofluoric acids is generally sufficient. To obtain satisfactory joints, the design must take into account the relatively low coefficient of expansion of titanium. Best practice calls for a design which will cause the metal with the highest coefficient of expansion to make the clearance larger rather than smaller during brazing. This will put the brazing alloy in compression during solidification.

The surface tension of titanium is low and the metal tends to absorb the filler metal faster than the adjacent dissimilar metal. This is serious when joining titanium to austenitic stainless steels. Difficulties can be overcome by plating the stainless steel with copper or iron or pretinning the steel with the brazing alloy.

DeCecco and Parks have reported the results of an extensive investigation of titanium brazing which included the development of suitable fluxes. They found that a large number of metals form brittle intermetallic compounds with titanium and thus joints made with these materials have limited applications. However, silver forms a ductile compound while aluminum forms two compounds, one ductile, the other brittle. As a result of these discoveries, ductile joints can be made with silver as the brazing material and it is possible to make fairly ductile joints using aluminum if rapid brazing times and relatively low temperatures are used.

In investigating fluxes it was found that molten silver chloride reacted with the titanium surface (as did other metallic chlorides) and deposited metal films which protected the surface from subsequent oxidation and released gaseous titanium tetrachloride. The tetrachloride assisted in disrupting nonmetallic films on the titanium. However, the pure chloride had a melting point which was too high for satisfactory use. A suitable flux was obtained by preparing a mixture of silver chloride, lithium fluoride or chloride, potassium chloride and sodium chloride.

Oxyacetylene-brazed single lap joints of commercial titanium brazed with fine silver, using silver chloride fluxes, broke with ductile fractures with shear strengths averaging 30,000 psi. Joints made similarly with 2S aluminum as the brazing metal showed a range in shear strength of about 12,000 to 27,000 psi. Those joints which broke at the lower end of the range had ductile fractures while the stronger joints broke with a brittle fracture.

Furnace brazed joints with silver as the brazing material can be made in impure inert atmospheres if silver chloride fluxes are used. Joint properties are equivalent to those obtained by torch brazing.

Titanium can be resistance brazed using water-cooled copper alloy anodes. With electrode pressure of 300 lb, high currents and short times (5 to 8 cycles), single lap joints brazed with fine silver had shear strengths up to 63,000 psi. No flux was necessary in making these joints.

Soft Soldering

DeCecco and Parks have reported also the results of a limited investigation of soft soldering. Commercial titanium was "tinned" by depositing films of copper, tin or silver from fused chloride salts on the surface in a helium atmosphere furnace. These films could be wet with 60-40 or 50-50 tin-lead solders using an ordinary soldering iron and a commercial flux. However, the soldering temperature and time required close control to prevent complete solution of the film in the solder. If this occurred, the solder dewetted and joints could not be made.

Silver films deposited by torch brazing were thicker than those deposited in a helium atmosphere. Commercial titanium covered with a thick film of this kind could be soldered to copper and failures occurred at the copper-solder interface rather than at the titanium interface.

Colner, Feinleib and Reding have also reported success in the soldering of titanium. They deposited a copper plate, electrolytically, on the surface of commercial titanium and one of the alloys and soft soldered copper strips to the titanium. In a number of cases, adherence was great enough to cause failure in the solder rather than at the interface.

These results indicate that suitable techniques for soldering titanium can be developed if the characteristics of the metal are considered.

Adhesive Bonding

With the coming of the jet engine and the increasing speed of aircraft, the designer has been faced with a number of new problems which required the use of new construction methods. As a consequence, the use of riveted construction is decreasing. In England particularly and to some extent in America, construction by adhesive bonding is receiving greater consideration because of the smoothness of the surfaces produced by this method and the increase in fatigue strength of bonded structures as compared with riveted assemblies.

Aero Research, in England, investigated the joining of commercial titanium with synthetic resins. The material was vapor degreased with trichlorethylene vapor and lightly abraded. The adhesive used was "Redux" which was cured under normal conditions 300° F for 20 min at 200 psi pressure. Single lap joints on material 1 in. wide made with a lap of 1 in. withstood 100,000 psi before failure.

In a second series of tests titanium and aluminum were joined by single lap joints using the same procedure. One inch lap joints failed in the aluminum under a load of 2450 lb.

Mechanical Fasteners

Brenner points out that the savings in weight which could be achieved by substituting titanium for steel in airframe construction make the metal attractive even at the present price. For example, on the basis of equivalent strength, 600 lb of titanium alloy structural fasteners could replace 1000 lb of steel fasteners in a typical airplane.

Several organizations have produced screws, bolts, nuts and rivets from commercial titanium. Screws, nuts and bolts have been produced from some of the alloys, also.

The galling and seizing which are characteristic of titanium make it difficult to run a nut on a bolt. In a test, a ½-20 titanium alloy bolt, torqued to 200 ft-lb developed a stress of 43,000 psi. The development of Teflon coating for threaded parts however has greatly improved the threading qualitites. A Teflon coated bolt of the same size torqued to 200 ft-lb developed a stress of 60,000 psi. This test indicates the amount of torque required to overcome friction on the untreated bolt and the good lubricating qualities of Teflon. Other expedients which have been used to overcome seizing and galling are allowing a slight oxide scale to remain on the fastener or applying a flash copper coating.

Riveting can be done on conventional equipment although there is some disagreement on the procedure. One organization states that the cold-upsetting of commercial titanium rivets is unsuccessful but normal heads are obtained by heating the rivet to about 1400° F before driving. Rivets formed in this manner had a shear strength of 73,000 psi.

Another report states that commercial titanium rivets can be driven with the same equipment used in driving aluminum alloy rivets. Close tolerance holes are necessary to obtain good upsetting of titanium rivets. However, riveting using the same gun and setting took about five times as long for titanium as for the aluminum alloy and upsetting pressure was about 1⅔ times as great. As a result, it is suggested that special rivet sets should be developed for driving titanium rivets and the shape of the rivets be modified. Driven under the same conditions, commercial titanium rivets (Ti-75A) had approximately 50 per cent greater shear strength than aluminum alloy 24ST rivets.

The use of titanium fasteners is still under development but at least two manufacturers have added them to their regular lists of products.

References

Holt, E. F., Vandenburgh, F. H. and McClymonds, N. L., "Spot Welding of Titanium-Carbon Alloys Containing 0.1, 0.4 and 0.6 Per Cent Carbon," *Welding Jour.*, 1057 (Nov., 1953).

Mahla, E. M. and Hitchcock, R. B., "Effect of Welding on Properties of Titanium-Carbon Alloys," *Welding Jour.*, 544S (Nov., 1950).

Martin, D. C., "Effects of Carbon, Oxygen and Nitrogen on Welds in Titanium," *Welding Jour.*, 139S (March, 1953).

Faulkner, G. E., Grable, G. B. and Voldrich, C. B., "The Effect of Alloying Elements on Welds in Titanium," *Welding Jour.*, 481S (Oct., 1953).

Barrett, J. C., Lane, Jr., I. R. and Huber, R. W., "Effect of Atmospheric Contaminants on Arc Welds in Titanium," *Welding Jour.*, 283S (June, 1953).

Nippes, E. F., Gerken, J. M., Schaaf, B. W. and Nelson, E. C., "Thermal Cycles in the Arc Welding of ½ in. Titanium Plate," *Welding Jour.*, 461S (Sept., 1953).

Begeman, M. L., Block, Jr., E. H. and McBee, Jr., F. W., "Spot Welding of Titanium Alloy Sheet," *Welding Jour.*, 469 (Oct., 1952).

Finlay, W. L., Jaffee, R. I., Parcel, R. W. and Durstein, R. C., "Tin Increases Strength of Ti-Al Alloys Without Loss in Fabricability," *Jour. Metals*, 25 (Jan., 1954).

Rosenberg, A. J., Hutchinson, E. F. and Weiss, S., "Restoration of Ductility in Alloy Titanium Welds," *Welding Jour.*, 708 (Aug., 1953).

Rosenberg, A. J., "Welding of Titanium," *Proc. Titanium Symposium*, Watertown Arsenal (Oct. 8, 1952).

Begeman, M. L., Block, Jr., E. H. and McBee, Jr., F. W., "Tension, Shear and Impact Strengths of Spot-Welded Titanium Joints," *Welding Jour.*, 599S (Dec., 1953).

Oehler, I. A., "Flash Welding Titanium Alloys," *Materials & Methods*, 206 (Sept., 1952).

Smith, L. W. and Yerkovich, L. A., "Strength of Joints in Titanium Brazed with Several Alloys," *Product Engineering*, 141 (July, 1953).

Meredith, H. L., "It's Easy to Braze Titanium," *American Machinist*, 120 (March 30, 1953).

DeCecco, N. A. and Parks, J. M., "The Brazing of Titanium," *Welding Jour.*, 1071 (Nov., 1953).

Anon., " 'Redux' Bonding of Titanium," *Light Metals*, 205 (June, 1953).

Brenner, H. S., "Titanium Fastener Development Report," *Fasteners*, 9, No. 2 (1953).

Colner, W. H., Feinleib, M. and Reding, J. N., "Electroplating on Titanium," *Jour. Electrochem. Soc.*, 100, 485 (1953).

Hughes, J. E., "Cold Pressure Welding of Titanium," *Sheet Metal Industries*, 52 (Jan., 1954).

8. MACHINING AND GRINDING

Procedures for the machining of metals have never been fully standardized and often differ widely from one plant to another. Although the type of chip formed when titanium is machined resembles that formed in machining the stainless steels there is considerable difference of opinion on the relative machinability of these materials. Some engineers state that titanium is more difficult to machine than stainless steels while others say that titanium is more readily machinable than stainless and claim that ease of machining increases with purity. Some of these differences may be the result of careless nomenclature. The term titanium has been used loosely to include the commercial metal and the alloys, materials which have quite different properties and can be expected to have different machinability ratings. One estimate of relative machinability rates titanium and its alloys in the 15 to 20 per cent range and 18-8 stainless steel at 25 per cent based on a rating of 100 per cent for SAE B1112 steel. Recent work in the aircraft industry has indicated that the alloys Ti-150A and MST 3Al-5Cr should be compared with the jet engine disk alloys rather than the stainless steels in relative machinability. However Fairbairn states that machining of titanium alloys is more difficult than machining type 347 stainless steel and compares them with Inconel X, a jet engine bucket alloy with less attractive machining characteristics than the disk alloys.

Dick reports that commercial titanium machines with greater difficulty than aluminum and about the same ease as the higher density stainless steels, and there seems to be general agreement that commercial titanium should be compared with the stainless steels.

Regardless of such comparisons which are, after all, only relative, suitable procedures are gradually being developed and with increasing knowledge, it is becoming apparent that machining is not such a difficult problem if the characteristics of the metal are taken into consideration.

Colwell and Truckenmiller point out that titanium has some rather unique machining properties. They list these as, (1) more superficial work hardening in titanium than in other metals, (2) little tendency to form a built-up edge, (3) relative to the thickness of the cut, thin chips are formed which increases the problems of pressure and temperature effects. On the other hand titanium and its alloys have the same specific energy consumption as medium carbon and low alloy steels. They note also that the relatively low cutting speeds required for optimum machining of titanium alloys tend to confirm the probability that higher temperatures and pressures exist. As an example under the same conditions, SAE 1045 can be machined at 187 sfm, RC-130B at 48 and Ti-150A at 74.

Krabacher and Merchant indicate that in machining SAE 1020, there is a low shear angle and a large built up edge, with SAE 1120, there is a high shear angle and no built up edge, and in machining Ti-150A there is an extremely high shear angle with no built up edge. On the other hand there is a rapid cyclic fluctuation of the shear angle, an inherent characteristic of titanium.

In comparing machinability of titanium alloy Ti-150A with SAE 1020, Merchant points out that there is a big difference in the bearing area between chip and tool when machining the two metals. The contact area on machining Ti-150A is only about half that when machining the steel. Therefore the bearing pressure is increased and in addition, frictional heat resulting from sliding of chip over the tool is concentrated in a smaller area. Since titanium has quite poor heat conductivity, the combination leads to extremely high tool temperatures, particularly on the part of the tool where the chip rubs. A comparison of tool temperatures under similar cutting conditions showed about 600° F on the bearing area when cutting SAE 1020 and about 2250° F on the titanium bearing area.

With temperatures in this range another factor enters. Practically all known metals and refractories are soluble in titanium. When the titanium chip is passing over the tool at such high temperatures, actual alloying occurs. The alloy is carried off with the chip and tool wear results. Alloying also has another effect. If the tool is stopped in contact with the work, a built up edge forms upon restarting, finish is poor, and titanium builds up on the tool face. This effect is produced by the alloying action between chip and tooth. If the temperature drops with the chip in contact with the tooth, the chip freezes to the tool face. On restarting the chip sticks to the tool and leaves a layer which is the beginning of a built-up edge. This effect, sometimes attributed to work-hardening is merely the alloying of the chip and tool and can be prevented by not allowing the chip to cool in contact with the tool.

Difficulties in milling are the direct result of this action. Chips tend to stick to the milling cutter face and upon the next contact with the work are knocked off taking chips of the tooth with them.

In cutting operations, positive feed must be maintained if satisfactory results are to be obtained. This prevents work hardening and glazing of the surface. The tool must not be allowed to ride on the work. Sharp cutting tools are essential to minimize work hardening and galling. Work must be held rigidly and tools must be kept sharp to allow a continuous positive cut.

In lathe turning, machines must be well supported and free from vibration. Tools should be held as close to the cutting edge as practical and long tool overhang avoided. On the rough turning of forgings, high speed steel tools operated with heavy feeds are satisfactory for commercial titanium while carbide tools are preferable for the titanium alloys. Slow speed with heavy feed apply also to such operations as milling, drilling, broaching and reaming.

For greatest machinability the material should contain less than 0.2 per cent carbon since this is the limit of solubility of carbon in titanium. If greater quantities of carbon are present, hard carbides introduce difficulties in maintaining sharp tools. Similarly, titanium should be free from nitrides and hard oxides also.

The force necessary to machine the material satisfactorily produces considerable heating which must be dissipated to prevent tool breakdown. The function of any cutting fluid in machining titanium is largely cooling.

Although some organizations are using the same cutting fluids in machining titanium as they use for other metals, better cutting fluids are being developed which should improve the machining process. Cutting oils containing sulfur additives have been effective in reducing seizing under severe cutting conditions. Others to which chlorinated solvents, such as carbon tetrachloride, have been added are more effective at low speeds and light cuts. Other compounds have been developed which contain active sulfur, active chlorine in non-toxic form, and polar type fatty additives combined with a mineral oil of the correct viscosity for the operation to be performed.

A method of directing small high speed jets of oil

at the point of contact between the work and the cutting edge has been reported to promote the rapid cutting of titanium in single-point tool operations.

Another development is the release of liquid carbon dioxide at the cutting edge. Using carbide tipped tools with carbon dioxide cooling, roughing cuts can be made at 120 sfm and finishing at 180 sfm. With high speed steel tools, these rates must be reduced to 35 sfm for roughing and 50 sfm for finishing. Others have reported using cutting speeds of more than 300 sfm with this method. Recently, however, it has been stated that this procedure is no more effective than the use of a suitable water-soluble cutting oil properly adjusted to the operation.

Summing up Boyd arrives at two definite requirements for the satisfactory cutting of titanium and its alloys. Extreme rigidity of the tool assembly and work is required and the cutting fluid must emphasize cooling rather than lubrication. He also points out that frequently laboratory or small scale tests do not indicate procedures which will be satisfactory on a large scale and it is advisable not to set up rigid cutting schedules without proving the methods on large scale tests.

Some of the methods which have been reported to give satisfactory results in machining operations are summarized briefly in the following pages. These procedures should be considered merely as suggestions which might require modification to suit the conditions existing in a specific plant.

Turning. Although relatively low cutting speeds are required, the turning of titanium and its alloys is not difficult with high speed steel, cast alloy or carbide tools. Heavy cuts are required and the tool must be in contact with the work continuously for good tool life at reasonable costs. The machine must be rigid and large enough to insure freedom from chatter and vibration.

Gauthier states that high speed steel tools are not sensitive to small changes in tool angles. He recommends 6 to 8 deg relief, 8 deg back rake, 15 deg side rake, 5 to 15 deg side cutting edges and 3/64 in. nose radius. He notes that chromium-plated high speed steel tools are no better than standard tools. Carbide tools are more influenced by changes in cutting edges than high speed steel tools. Using water soluble cutting fluids, heavy feeds and rigid machines, he sets the upper limit of cutting speed at 30 sfm for high speed steel and 150 to 300 sfm for carbide tools when cutting commercial and alloy titanium.

For the turning of Ti-150A and RC-130B, Coughlin suggests carbide tools with a negative rake angle of 5 deg and a large chip contact area. With the combination of heavy cuts, slow speeds and a water soluble cutting oil with a 10 to 1 ratio, good tool life is obtained. Work and tool must be held rigidly and, in turning between centers, live centers are desirable since dead centers cause galling and seizing.

Turning tests on Ti-150A, RC-130B and MST 3Al-5Cr were compared with those on stainless and alloy steels by Zlatin. Using tungsten carbide tools, allowable speeds for a tool life of 20 min were, 100 fm for MST3Al-5Cr, 180 fm for RC-130B and 200 fm for Ti-150A. With high speed steel tools the corresponding values were 30 fm for RC-130B and 45 for Ti-150A. It was not practical to cut MST3Al-5Cr with high speed steel tools. To furnish a comparison, stainless grades 410 and 347 can be cut at speeds 3 to 4 times those used for Ti-150A, while SAE 4340, heat treated to the same hardness level as Ti-150A can be machined twice as fast.

Milling. Milling is a more difficult problem than turning because of the nature of the operation. The cutter mills only during a part of each revolution and the chip remains welded to the tooth during the remainder. As the tooth enters the cut during the next cycle, the chip is knocked off together with a bit of the tool.

Coughlin recommends the use of heavy cuts, low speeds and coarse feeds on a rugged machine with ample power. Best results were obtained using 18-4-2 high speed steel tools with 3 deg relief, 0 deg rake, and 0.010 to 0.015 in. land. A 45 deg chamfer on the cutter helps to dissipate heat.

On the other hand, Zlatin suggests cast alloy tools. He notes that the relief angle is critical and a 12 deg angle is better than 6 deg. He suggests that less chipping of the cutting edge occurs if light feeds of 0.004 to 0.008 in. per tooth are used. He also notes that carbide tools with a negative rake angle of 10 deg give reasonable tool life if a suitable

144

cutting fluid is used with cutting speeds of 50 to 70 fm.

Face milling is the most satisfactory procedure for use whenever it can be employed. Speeds of 90 sfm have been used for face milling RC-130B and 180 sfm for commercial titanium.

Drilling. In the drilling of titanium alloys it is essential to maintain a positive feed at all times and not to allow the tool to ride on the work. Slow speed and heavy feed are advisable and the unsupported portion of the drill should be as short as possible. No pilot holes should be used.

In one organization the use of either standard or high cobalt high speed steels is recommended. The drills are resharpened to give an included angle of 130 to 137 deg with a lip clearance of 10 to 12 deg. Using a paste lubricant of sulfurized lanolin, speeds of 20 sfm and feeds of 0.006 in. per revolution were satisfactory with standard high speed steel. With cobalt high speed steel tools, speeds of 60 sfm and feeds of 0.006-0.012 in. per revolution gave satisfactory results with high pressure oil lubrication.

In another company, the drill is sharpened to have a 130 deg point angle, 35 deg helix angle and a 10 deg lip relief. It is ground with a notch. Using a heavy sulfur base oil, satisfactory results were obtained at speeds of 20 sfm with feeds of 0.006 to 0.009 in. per revolution depending on the diameter. This organization also notes that drill jigs of conventional design require twice as much clearance between the work and the drill bushing for titanium drilling as is customarily used for steel.

Tapping. The tapping of titanium and its alloys is one of the more difficult machining operations. Trouble is experienced in cooling the work and lubricating the teeth and in disposing of the chips. As a result galling and seizing of the tap or build-up on the cutting edge occur and tap breakage is a problem. Thread requirements of 60 to 70 per cent give the best results. Optimum thread engagement is 1½ the tap diameter.

In one organization best results were obtained using a three flute tap, having a four thread chamfer, every other tooth removed, and a 10 deg hook angle. In another, 18-4-1 high speed steel taps with a hook angle of 6 to 8 deg and a cutting angle of 11 to 12 deg were used. The tap had full eccentric relief, and a point diameter equivalent to 83⅓ per cent of the thread. A sulfurized cutting fluid with or without chlorine additives gave good results in tapping alloy grades of titanium at a speed of 20 sfm.

External Thread Cutting. The cutting of external threads should be done by turning or chasing in a lathe if possible, since welding of the work to the die has been reported if attempts are made to thread with dies. Commercial titanium bolts have been threaded with standard tangential chasers at a rate of 72 rpm with difficulty.

Reaming. Carbide tipped reamers having 4 flutes, with a back taper of 0.0002 in. per in. of flat, a primary clearance angle of 10 to 15 deg and a 45 deg chamfer have been found satisfactory for production reaming. Speeds of 40 to 70 rpm and feeds between 0.008 and 0.020 in. per revolution are suggested using a sulfur and chlorine additive cutting oil. High speed steel tools operating at 10 to 12 fpm with feeds of about 0.008 in. per revolution have also worked satisfactorily.

Broaching. Broaching is probably the most difficult of the machining operations. Cobalt high speed steel is recommended as superior to standard high speed steel. For best results in machining the alloys, the material should be no harder than Rockwell C37, since material of higher hardness tends to bind and resist broaching. It is suggested that the grinding of broaches is a critical operation because it is desirable to produce a tool on which each tooth load is between 0.003 and 0.005 in. Rigid tool set-up is absolutely necessary and broaching should be performed in one pass. Sulfurized oils are serving well as lubricants.

Sawing. Titanium and its alloys are difficult to saw, particularly in large sections. Heavy positive cuts are desirable. Satisfactory results have been obtained with various machine saws when the work was flooded with a soluble oil and water coolant.

Extremely coarse blades are suggested, having 2 to 4 teeth per in. with feeds of 0.009 to 0.12 in. for hack saws having positive hydraulic feed. For friction feed saws, blades with 6 teeth per in. and feeds of about 0.015 in. give good results. In both cases flooding the work with a standard cutting oil is necessary to remove the chips and cool the work.

In slotting commercial titanium machine screws, a 36 tooth saw operating at 116 rpm has been used.

The work was cooled with a soluble oil (ratio 20 to 1). Slotting at the rate of 45 pieces per minute showed no evidence of unusual tool wear or welding of chips to the cutting edge on an experimental production of 1000 pieces.

Abrasive Cut-off. Wet abrasive cut-off wheels are recommended by some organizations as the best method of cutting titanium. For successful cutting the work should be rotated in order that the wheel can cut toward the center and is not required to cut entirely through the piece. Oscillating the wheel is also helpful. It has been reported that 7 in. dia bars have been cut by this procedure in 10 min while ½ in. bars have been cut in a few seconds.

Flame Cutting. Heavy titanium sections can be flame cut readily. The smoothest cuts are obtained if the operations are performed at high speed with the least possible preheating. Two in. square sections have been cut at 140 in. per min. To avoid thermal cracking of flame-cut surfaces, the material should be annealed at 1100° F for about 1 hr and air cooled.

Grinding

Machining and grinding are closely related operations. Consequently, the same basic problems are encountered. They include, (1) the low thermal conductivity of titanium, (2) solubility of the abrasive in titanium at high temperatures and (3) the high velocity of chip flow. The combination of high velocity and low conductivity leads to high temperatures with the result that the abrasive is dissolved by the titanium. This was a particularly troublesome problem in the early days of titanium fabrication because attempts to use the conditions developed for grinding steel resulted in excessive wheel wear.

Rideout has discussed methods developed to improve the grinding of titanium. In the early stages of the work a "grinding ratio" was established to permit evaluation of the methods under consideration. This ratio is the metal removed in cubic inches per cubic inch of wheel wear.

Operations using normal grinding speeds gave a ratio of 0.7. By decreasing the speed, it was possible to obtain a three fold improvement in the grinding ratio. By using this reduced speed in combination with a suitable cutting fluid, the grinding ratio was raised to about 15. This compares with a ratio of 3 to 4 for high carbon high chromium tool steels, 4 to 12 for 18-4-1 high speed steel and 40 to 80 for carbon and low alloy steels. Thus the present ratio for titanium alloys is far higher than that for a high vanadium high speed steel (0.4 to 1) which was used as a standard of comparison for titanium in the early days of grinding.

The grinding of titanium is quite different from the grinding of steel in the type of wheel wear which results. With steel, the greater part of wheel wear is caused by breaking of the bonding agent. With titanium most of the wear results from attrition probably as the result of actual solution of the abrasive in the titanium. By reducing the wheel speed and using a suitable coolant, the temperature at the contact point is lowered and attrition is reduced, thus increasing the grinding ratio.

Aluminum oxide wheels are considered best for grinding titanium and its alloys, at present, although soft-bonded silicon carbide is preferred by at least one organization. Since titanium dust, like that of the other light metals, is explosive, wet grinding procedures should be employed. Wet grinding assists also in preventing thermal cracking caused by localized overheating.

For the surface grinding of RC-130B and Ti-150A, Rideout recommends using a vitrified bonded alumina wheel, with size 60 to 80 grit, the grade of wheel being as hard as it is possible to use without burning or smearing the material. The wheel speed should be about 1600 sfm and the table speed 200 to 400 in. per min. A suitable coolant is necessary. Under these conditions, it is possible to obtain a surface finish of 35 to 45 microinches, rms.

For surface grinding of MST3Al-5Cr, the producer recommends a hard alumina wheel similar to that mentioned above, a wheel speed of 1200 sfm and a table speed of 400 to 500 in. per min with a down feed of not more than 0.001 in. per pass. Sulfurized and chlorinated cutting oils have produced some of the best results but straight grinding oils, rust inhibitors and soluble oils have all been used.

Krabacher and Merchant have also investigated the grinding of titanium alloys and their recommendations are somewhat different. For surface grinding they suggest using an alumina wheel, running at a speed of 5000 sfm with an effective grinding fluid. Using the definite set of conditions described in their report they were able to obtain grinding ratios of 72 to 114 in. grinding Ti-150A and suggest that similar results could be obtained with RC-130B. They point out however that the hardness has a definite effect on the grinding ratio and a limit of about Rockwell C37 to 38 should be set. In attempting to grind Ti-150A with a hardness of Rockwell C42, glazing and chattering occurred.

On internal grinding, the same investigators using plunge grinding with a suitable wheel and flooding the contact area with a coolant obtained grinding ratios of 70 to 100.

It would appear therefore that the problems of grinding titanium economically are being rapidly solved and standard procedures for these operations will be set up by the producers of the grinding equipment.

References

Anon., "Increased Production Reduced Costs Through a Better Understanding of the Machining Process and Control of Materials Tools Machines," *Curtis-Wright Corp.*, **2** (1951).

Fairbairn, G. A., "Working Titanium at North American," *Machinery,* 182 (July, 1953).

Dick, J. N., "Titanium and The Air Force," *Modern Metals,* 35 (May, 1952).

Colwell, L. V. and Truckenmiller, W. C., "Cutting Characteristics of Titanium and Its Alloys," *Mechanical Engineering,* 461 (June, 1953).

Krabacher, E. J. and Merchant, M. E., "Fundamental

Factors in the Machining and Grinding of Titanium," *ASME* paper presented at New York Meeting (Dec., 1953).

Merchant, M. E., "Fundamental Facts on Machining Titanium," *Proc. Titanium Symposium,* Watertown Arsenal, 33 (Oct. 8, 1952).

Boyd, J. A., "Be Cagey with Titanium," *American Machinist,* 129 (Sept. 14, 1953).

Gauthier, V. L., "Guideposts to Titanium Cutting," *Steel,* 76 (Mar. 23, 1953).

Coughlin, V. L., "How GE Works Titanium," *American Machinist,* 176 (Feb. 16, 1953).

Zlatin, N., "Turning and Milling of Titanium," *Proc. Titanium Symposium,* Watertown Arsenal, 32 (Oct. 8, 1952).

Goldberg, D. C. and Hazelton, W. S., "How to Machine Titanium," *Iron Age,* 107 (April 17, 1952).

Jamilkowski, V., "Tapping of Titanium," *Proc. Titanium Symposium,* Watertown Arsenal, 29 (Oct. 8, 1952).

Brenner, H. S., "Titanium Fastener Development Report," *Fasteners,* 9, No. 2 (1953).

Rideout, G. T., "Grinding of Titanium," *Proc. Titanium Symposium,* Watertown Arsenal, 25 (Oct. 8, 1952).

9. CLEANING AND FINISHING

With the exception of information on descaling and pickling, methods of cleaning and finishing titanium have received little attention in the literature. However, conventional methods can be used for the removal of oils, greases and dirt. On the other hand, titanium is such a reactive metal that particles of impurities adhering to the surface as a result, for example, of sand blasting could react with the metal upon subsequent heat treatment to cause hardening of the surface layers and introduce difficulties in subsequent fabrication.

Plating on titanium is difficult and only recently have procedures been developed which indicate that the problem is nearing a solution.

Salt Bath Descaling

A major problem in the use of titanium alloys is the removal of scale formed during forging, hot rolling and heat treatment. Durkin points out that solubility of scale in both acids and alkalies depends on its temperature of formation. Thus, oxide

153

formed below about 1300° F is theoretically soluble in concentrated sulfuric acid, solubility in both mineral acids and molten salts decreases rapidly as the temperature is increased and oxide formed above 1830° F is theoretically insoluble. He notes that from the industrial point of view, any oxide formed above 1400° F is practically insoluble in common acid and alkali descaling solutions.

For the removal of tough scale, Durkin recommends the use of the Virgo salt process or the Kolene No. 4 process, the latter operated either as a dip or electrolytic bath. He states that metal losses are small in either of these baths and no loss in ductility occurred in titanium processed for 30 min in the range 800 to 1000° F. This is in distinct contrast with descaling in molten sodium hydroxide. To be effective, such baths must operate at high temperatures with the result that high metal losses occur and there is danger of embrittlement, particularly if temperatures above 850° F are used.

Sodium hydride descaling can be used to remove mill scale from hot rolled titanium according to Sittig. Plates up to 1 in. thick and sheets as thin as 0.015 in. have been successfully descaled by this treatment, which, because of the low temperature employed, eliminates the problem of burning of thin sheet during drag-out before water-quenching. The bath consists of sodium hydroxide containing 2 per cent of sodium hydride. Metal is immersed in the hydride bath for about 15 min at a temperature of 680 to 700° F, water quenched, washed in 8 per cent sulfuric acid at 100° F for 1 min, washed in 6 per cent nitric-1 per cent hydrofluoric acid mixture at room temperature for ½ min and rinsed in water. He reports that there is no danger of hydrogen embrittlement at the temperature used.

Durkin introduces a note of caution on the operation of molten salt baths. If the temperature in any of these baths is allowed to rise above 1000° F, there is danger that the titanium will react violently with the bath and fires or explosions will occur.

Acid Pickling

The use of acid pickling to follow salt bath descaling has been mentioned above. Acids are used also in certain other procedures.

Acid pickling is highly effective in the removal of light scale from titanium. One recommended treatment is immersion in 15 per cent sulfuric acid at room temperature for 10 to 15 min, rinse in water, dip in a 3 to 1 nitric-hydrofluoric acid solution at 140 to 160° F for 1 to 3 min, rinse in water.

Another pickling solution is composed of hydrochloric and hydrofluoric acids. Dipping at room temperature for 2 to 4 min in a solution of this kind is reported to remove scale. However, the surface is etched slightly.

Mechanical and Chemical Cleaning

During fabrication, metal surfaces often become coated with oils, greases, metallic particles, dirt and similar materials. There are a number of methods by which cleaning can be accomplished. According to Campbell, cleaning methods suitable for titanium and its alloys include blast cleaning, brushing, alkali or emulsion cleaning, electrolytic cleaning, steam cleaning, solvent cleaning and vapor degreasing.

Petersen points out that sand blasting, wire brushing and some special rolling techniques contaminate commercial titanium to a measurable extent and the surface characteristics must be considered if the finished product is to be of high quality.

Blast Cleaning. Titanium scale can be removed mechanically by grit or vapor blasting if a matte finish is permissible. The process is usually employed for cleaning heavy sections such as rods, bars, plates and forgings but vapor blasting has been used to prepare surfaces for welding or brazing.

When titanium is sand-blasted, fine particles of silica are embedded in the surface. On subsequent heat treatment, these particles react with the metal and diffuse inward, producing a hardened skin which affects subsequent forming operations adversely. Embedded particles of silica can be removed by pickling the surface in a dilute nitrichydrofluoric acid pickle immediately after sand blasting.

Wire Brushing. Wire brushing can be used for removing loose scale, organic and inorganic matter and burrs from the titanium surface. For best results a soft flexible wire brush is suggested.

If titanium is wire brushed, particles of steel adhere to the surface. These will cause iron contamination upon subsequent heating. A nitric-hydrofluoric acid pickle before heating will remove the iron from the surface and prevent contamination.

Alkali Cleaning. A common method of cleaning is agitation in a bath containing an alkali. Proprietary mixtures of caustic soda, potash, phosphates, silicates and similar alkalies together with organic emulsifiers and synthetic wetting agents are used most commonly. The bath is violently agitated to loosen the dirt while the alkali saponifies the animal and vegetable oils and emulsifies the mineral oils, thus removing them from the surface. Solutions often contain from 4 to 8 oz of cleaner per gallon of water and the bath is operated at temperatures ranging from 140 to 190° F.

Electrolytic Cleaning. Electrolytic cleaning can be used for many parts for which hand scrubbing is not suitable. Alkali cleaners similar to those used in the mechanical cleaning method are used. However, no emulsifiers or wetting agents are included in the bath because of the possibility of excessive foaming. The work should be made the cathode.

Emulsion Cleaning. Emulsion cleaning solutions operate in the same manner as the alkali cleaners. The cleaning agent consists of hydrocarbon solvents containing emulsifying and wetting agents. The bath is violently agitated to assist in removal of contaminants. Temperature of operation ranges from room to 160° F depending on the boiling point of the solvent.

Steam Cleaning. Steam cleaning is a modification

of either alkali or emulsion cleaning. In this method the cleaner is carried in a jet of steam and impinges on the surface at high velocity. Steam pressures of 50 to 150 lb are used with ½ to 4 oz per gallon of alkali cleaner or ½ to 5 per cent by volume of emulsion cleaner.

Solvent Cleaning. Solvent cleaning is particularly adaptable for use on machined parts to remove cutting oil. The material is immersed in a suitable solvent, usually a low-boiling mineral oil fraction held, generally at temperatures of the order of 120 to 140° F.

Vapor Degreasing. Vapor cleaning, generally with trichlorethylene as the solvent is a rapid method of removing oils from the surface of a part. The material to be cleaned is placed in a suitable chamber in which the solvent vapor can be condensed. The condensate removes oil from the surface and leaves the material clean and dry.

Electroplating

Attempts to plate dissimilar metals on titanium have met with indifferent success until recently. Titanium is a highly active metal and its excellent corrosion resistance depends on the formation of a strongly adherent oxide film on the surface. This film interferes when attempts are made to deposit other metals on the surface and it is hard to remove. In at least one organization, plating over an oxidized coating has been reported to have given good results. However, the substitution of nonaqueous plating baths for conventional types has been the first real development in solving the problem of plating on titanium.

One of the producers of titanium obtains an adherent coating of copper on titanium after deliberately developing an oxide film. Hot-rolled titanium is cleaned with one of the alkali salt baths mentioned previously, washed and annealed in air at 1225 to 1325° F to produce an oxide film. The copper plate is deposited from a cyanide bath in about 30 min.

Some success has been reported in the chromium plating of titanium using a hot chromium plating solution together with a reducing flux, while other methods have also been mentioned although no details have been disclosed.

Colner, Feinleib and Reding have developed a method of electroplating which yields adherent deposits. The primary requirement in their process is the production of an etched surface to which the electrodeposit adheres mechanically.

To obtain physical and chemical cleanliness, the metal is degreased cathodically in an alkaline bath, then pickled in a nitric-hydrofluoric acid bath.

Anodic etching follows in a bath based on ethylene glycol and hydrofluoric acid. Etching requires about 15 to 30 min with a current density of about 50 amp per sq ft at a temperature of 125 to 140° F. Cathodes of a nonreacting material such as graphite, nickel or copper are used. Best results are obtained if the bath is agitated and the titanium is removed while the current flow continues to avoid local action.

Following etching, the material is rinsed, given a copper strike in a copper cyanide bath at room temperature and plated in a copper fluoborate bath also at room temperature.

In spite of the fact that the plating was done on a rough surface, as high as 50 microinches rms, the throwing power of the bath was such that the heavier plates had surfaces almost as smooth as those of other metals which had been electrodeposited on a smooth base.

Adhering copper plates, 0.0005 to 0.005 in. in thickness were produced. These plates passed bending and flexing tests for adherence and could be soldered readily. Soldered joints often failed in the solder rather than at the interface. Incidentally, their work showed that adhering deposits could not be obtained on a smooth titanium surface.

This procedure was used in depositing copper coatings on Ti-75A, RC-70 and RC-130B. Having developed a method of obtaining adhering copper plates, there should be little difficulty in using normal plating methods to deposit other metals on the copper.

Electropolishing.

Colner, Feinleib and Reding report that titanium can be electropolished in a bath consisting essentially of ethylene glycol which contains small percentages of hydrofluoric acid and water. They recommend operating the bath at room or only slightly elevated temperatures using current densities of 75 to 100 amps per sq ft. Under these conditions, a surface finish of 2.5 microinches rms was obtained. It should be noted that this work was done on a laboratory scale.

Commercial electropolishing of titanium has not been reported.

Anodizing

Titanium can be anodized readily to produce films of various colors which depend on the thickness of the oxide film. Anodizing can be accomplished at about 85° F in various solutions, for example 15 per cent sulfuric acid for 10 min at 10 volts. To obtain satisfactory results the surface must be degreased and it is reported that a light pickle in hydrofluoric acid will improve the uniformity of the colors produced. The film resulting from this anodizing treatment makes the surface quite passive.

References

Durkin, A. E., "How To Descale Titanium," *Materials & Methods*, 107 (Oct., 1953).

Sittig, M., "Titanium Descaled Successfully with Sodium Hydride," *Iron Age*, 137 (Dec. 17, 1953).

Campbell, J. B., "Selecting Metal Cleaning Methods," *Materials & Methods*, 119 (Nov., 1953).

Peterson, V. C., "Surface Contamination and Quality in Titanium Fabrication," *Materials & Methods*, 72 (July, 1953).

Colner, W. H., Feinleib, M. and Reding, J. N., "Electroplating on Titanium," *Jour. Electrochem Society*, **100**, 485 (1953).

10. APPLICATIONS

Although titanium has been suggested for practically every imaginable service, the fields in which it will find its major applications are now rather clearly defined. Applications are based on several distinctive properties of this material. These are:

(1) Strength. Titanium alloys are from 2 to 3 times as strong as aluminum alloys, 5 times as strong as magnesium alloys and stronger than some of the alloy steels.

(2) Stiffness. Titanium is stiffer than either aluminum or magnesium. Its modulus of elasticity while roughly half that of steel, is considerably higher than those of aluminum or magnesium.

(3) Light weight. Titanium is roughly half as heavy as steel.

(4) Strength/weight ratio. The combination of high strength and light weight is probably the most important property of titanium and its alloys. The strength/weight ratios of these materials are among the best available. For equal strength, savings in weight up to 40 per cent can be achieved by replacing steel with titanium.

Jaffee notes that titanium will find its major applications because of this high ratio, which can be illustrated by a series of tests made on compressor disks of the same size to determine their bursting speed. An aluminum disk weighing 25 lb burst at a speed of 20,000 rpm, a stainless steel disk, weigh-

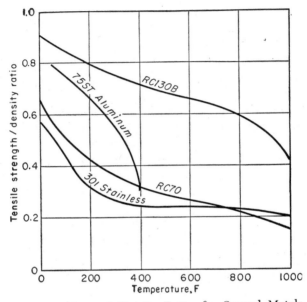

Fig. 10-1. Strength-Density Ratios for Several Metals (Rem-Cru)

ing 30 lb burst at 17,000 rpm while a titanium alloy disk made of RC-130B weighing 17 lb did not burst at 25,000 rpm.

(5) Corrosion resistance. In contact with many corroding media, titanium has shown corrosion re-

163

sistance equal to or better than austenitic stainless steel while in resistance to salt water corrosion it is comparable to platinum.

These properties of titanium and its alloys will lead to their use in the following military and civilian services when the metal becomes available in sufficient quantity.

The major applications for many years will probably be in the field of aviation for, (1) airframe skins and structures in the intermediate temperature range, and (2) aircraft power plants for temperatures up to 1000° F.

Military applications in ordnance and other equipment where a combination of light weight, good strength and corrosion resistance is required will probably account for a considerable quantity of titanium until the price is reduced.

A broad field is open in naval and marine applications because titanium has outstanding resistance to sea water corrosion but this field is pretty well closed until the price of the metal is reduced considerably.

Finally, the corrosion resistance of titanium points to broad usage in industrial equipment at some time in the future, a promise which is being fulfilled on a limited scale today.

Aircraft Applications

Dick states that in aircraft applications particularly in military planes, titanium is needed wherever it is possible to save weight and thus achieve increased pay loads or an increase in range. Thus the Air Force is interested in using the metal or its alloys in everything from engines to airframes and even in such simple parts as bolts and nuts.

It is generally considered that the saving of 1 lb in the engine makes it possible to save from 8 to 10 lb in overall weight of the airplane and each pound saved in the airframe makes the airplane more maneuverable.

In jet engines, titanium is being used chiefly in the compressor as disks and blading. Among the alloys which have been investigated for this service are Ti-150A, Ti-140A and RC-130B. Materials being replaced by titanium in this application include cold-worked 18 per cent chromium-8 per cent nickel and 12 per cent chromium stainless steels and heat treated alloy steels.

Although the major use of titanium in jet engines has been in compressor disks and blades, the use of sheet metal parts for such applications as combustion chamber liners is planned. These liners would require a material having a yield strength of 120,000 psi at room temperature and 60,000 psi at 600° F. The material would also have to be weldable and the resulting welds be ductile. The only commercial material approaching these requirements at present is A-110AT.

The major uses for titanium in the fuselage of aircraft is in parts which will be subjected to temperatures of the order of 250° F. Commercial titanium because of its availability in sheet form, ease of fabrication and weldability is in industrial use at present for shroud assemblies, ammunition tracks, and cable shrouds. RC-130B has been used for bulkheads and fuselage frames and alloy ribs are in use for stiffeners and highly stressed parts.

Beardman states that the Navy is now using titanium in naval aircraft in the form of forgings, tubing, sheet and strip of both commercial and alloy grades. In the engine, forgings of these materials are in use for compressor disks, spacers, and blades while tubing serves for compressor rotor disk spacer tubes. In the airframe, uses of sheet include: door installation of main landing gear, center wing structure, center wing front bulkhead, shrouds, various fuselage parts, firewalls and flame seals. Floor and door assemblies for helicopters are also being made of titanium sheet. Strip is being used for engine access panel assembly cases, link door assemblies, cabin air valve guard assemblies and electronic access door assemblies.

The Bureau of Aeronautics is also considering the following production uses of titanium and titanium alloys: forgings for landing gear components, compressor blades and disks; sheet for such parts as turbine liners, baffles, skin assembly, tail cones and engine shrouds; bars for compressor bolts and miscellaneous hardware. Other possible applications include vaporizing plates, armor plate, propeller blades, compressor running rings and compressor couplings.

Turning now to specific airplanes, reports of actual replacement of other materials by titanium are being issued with increasing frequency.

In the DC-7 titanium was substituted for stainless steel, gage for gage, without serious fabricating problems in some nacelles and firewalls. Now, approximately 88 per cent of the skin of the engine nacelles consists of commercial titanium sheet. Eventually all of the nacelles on the DC-7 will be titanium. Douglas is using 528 lb of titanium per plane and by so doing is saving 200 lb in weight. This is an important saving because it is estimated that every lb saved is worth $40 in additional pay load. Douglas is now using from 1 to 3 per cent of the weight in titanium and expects to increase this figure to more than 20 per cent in three years.

Large parts of the skin of the Douglas X-3 supersonic airplane are made of commercial titanium especially those parts which are exposed to engine heat or are heated aerodynamically. Titanium was selected for this service because aluminum alloys lose strength above 300° F and stainless steel is too heavy.

In North American's jet airplane, FJ-2, commercially pure titanium is being used for shroud assemblies, cable shrouds, ammunition tracks and flap-rubbing strips while RC-130A is used for fuselage frames and bulkheads. North American is also using 1 per cent titanium in the F-86 and 5 per cent in the F-100 now.

Other reports state that production models of jet planes now contain as much as 600 lb of titanium and titanium alloys in the form of sheet, bar and forgings.

Republic is experimenting with titanium ammunition boxes to replace steel in the F84F fighter bomber. Replacement of six boxes would save 25 lb. Under development also is the shroud which surrounds the jet engine tail pipe to protect the airplane from engine heat. In this application replacement of steel by titanium would save 50 lb. Other probable applications are cockpit armor and fasteners.

Interest in titanium fasteners has been sufficient to lead several manufacturers into their production. Double hexagon stopnuts of titanium-alloy now in production in sizes from 5/16 to ⅝ in. meet the tensile requirements for steel but weigh less than ½ as much. In one type of fighter plane, it has been estimated that the replacement of steel fasteners by titanium would save over 200 lb. This would mean a saving of about 1 ton overall since as mentioned previously engineers estimate that every pound saved in structural design weight permits an overall reduction in weight of 10 lb.

A modified dowel pin rivet is in production from MST3Al-5Cr. The pin has a collar of 24ST aluminum "set" on one end to create a manufactured head. After insertion, a second 24ST aluminum collar is "set" onto the pin with conventional equipment.

Future Developments

In the temperature range 300 to 800° F titanium retains a much higher proportion of its room temperature strength than do either aluminum or magnesium. This is the range in which titanium will be used most widely for some time to come.

Titanium tubing has been suggested for use in airplane hydraulic lines which must be light in weight but withstand peak pressures up to 6000 psi. At present these lines are made of stainless steel tubing. As it is difficult to flare the ends of titanium tubing in the field, fittings have been devised which do not require the flaring of the tube.

Sweet states that to realize the potentials of titanium in airframe construction, stronger sheet alloys with better fabricating properties must be developed. He suggests that an all purpose alloy to replace high strength aluminum should have the formability of annealed 75S aluminum and be capable of developing a tensile strength near 175,000 psi, a yield strength of about 90 per cent of the tensile strength and an elongation of 10 to 15 per cent. It should be weldable by spot welding. Other alloys in sheet form should have tensile strengths of about 150,000 psi, with a 90 per cent yield strength and 15 per cent elongation, should have good ductility after welding and be readily formed at both room and elevated temperatures. He suggests that such alloys could compete with low alloy steel heat treated to 180,000 psi and replace stainless steel in welded construction in applications at temperatures up to 800° F. Alloys with similar strength properties which were spot weldable would be suitable for skins in supersonic airplanes.

For fuel tanks in missiles, corrosion resistance to fuming nitric acid is necessary. Sweet suggests that a suitable alloy should have a tensile strength of 120,000 psi, yield strength of 110,000 psi and elongation of 15 per cent and should be capable of being deep drawn and of being welded satisfactorily. The alloy would require corrosion resistance equivalent to that of commercial titanium.

Military Applications

Mesick points out that military applications in the early stages of development will be designed to save weight. The widely publicized mortar base plate is a case in point. Originally made of steel in two sections, each weighing 24 lb and requiring two men to transport it, this base plate was redesigned to be made of ⅛ or 1/10 in. commercial titanium. The titanium base plate weighs only 24 lb and can be carried by one man. All types of standard equipment carried by the individual soldier are under review with the object of using titanium to reduce the weight.

Reed notes that flash suppressors for artillery are made of steel and are often so heavy that the gun efficiency is impaired. Titanium flash suppressors are light enough so they do not impair the efficiency of the gun but are sufficiently strong to withstand the forces imposed when the gun is fired.

Other gun components for which commercial titanium is under consideration are field gun mount trails which serve to carry the firing stresses to the ground and anti-aircraft gun outriggers to prevent excessive tipping during firing. These components are made of steel at present. An alloy grade of titanium is being considered for use in a new design of gun mount which will be 30 to 35 per cent lighter than one of equal strength made of steel.

As a result of ballistic tests, development of titanium armor for vehicles is in progress. Vehicles equipped with this armor can be at least 25 per cent lighter than those equipped with steel armor or, by using the same weight, can offer greater protection to the operating personnel.

Titanium is replacing brass in certain primer cups because of its greater resistance to chemical action. The specific application is restricted information.

Titanium is also being considered for use in airborne missiles. It would reduce the weight of the missile if it replaced stainless steel. Since it retains its strength to higher temperatures than aluminum or magnesium, it is more valuable for service under conditions of high speed flight where aerodynamic heating can increase the temperature of the missile to quite high values.

Weight saving is also important in projectiles and consideration is being given to titanium for future use in this field. It has been estimated that the range of certain shells might be increased as much as 35 per cent if they were made of titanium instead of steel.

Other uses contemplated by the military are bridges, cylinders for storage and transportation of compressed gases and air strip landing mats.

Marine Service

Even at present prices, the Navy believes that there are some uses for titanium which are economical. Such applications would meet the following requirements: (1) titanium is the only material having the desired properties; (2) the price of the metal is small compared to the fabricating cost of the equipment; and (3) a great increase in service life would result from the application of titanium.

The Navy is investigating titanium for such service as the following: wet exhaust mufflers for submarine diesel engines because replacement is a major operation and present materials have limited service life; meter disks for service in oil, gasoline and salt water meters since no material completely satisfactory for service under all of these conditions has been found. Thin wall condenser and heat exchanger tubes for extremely high water velocities are also under investigation. The suitability of titanium for heat exchanger tubes in closed cycle engines is being determined. These tubes must be highly resistant to corrosion by sea water on one side and exhaust condensate on the other. Materials such as bronze and monel have definite life limitations in high velocity salt water systems and it is hoped that titanium will prove superior to these more conventional materials. Other applications are based on resistance to marine atmospheres possibly contaminated by stack gases such as are met in antenna wires.

The Bureau of Ships is not considering the use of titanium on any large scale at present but it is testing the alloys for various possible future applications. Actual use will depend on a number of factors, not the least of which for many applications is price. Among such parts are: bars for turbine blades in low temperature steam turbines; permanent mold castings for wear rings in salt water pumps, valve bodies, seats and disks for salt water service; plate for snorkel pipe in submarine snorkel systems, and hot water tanks in machinery equipment; and tubing for salt water valves, condensers and heat exchangers.

Other parts which are under consideration but have not yet reached the testing stage are bars for control shafts in electronic equipment, radar antennas, and propeller shafts in mine sweeper propulsion equipment; castings for microwave cavities in frequency meters, pump impellers for salt water service, fire hose nozzles for firefighting equipment, deck fittings for submarine electrical equipment; plate for radar wave guides, navigation light shields and machinery vents; powder for compressor blades in gas turbines; sheet for shock mounts in machinery, radar antenna and deck equipment; tubing for radar antennas, microwave cavities in frequency meters; wire for resistance wire in electronic equipment.

Corrosion Resistance

The applications of titanium in marine service have been discussed previously. Although little information has been published on the resistance of the metal to attack under plant service conditions and the selection of materials on the basis of laboratory corrosion experiments is dangerous, it appears probable that one of the major fields of usage of titanium will be for corrosion resisting equipment in the process industries. Only limited material has been available for such service up to the present time but applications are already being found for the metal where some of the more readily available materials have had unsatisfactory life. Although only the surface has been scratched, a few applications have been reported.

Commercial titanium is in use on a limited scale in equipment for handling 22 per cent sulfuric acid under high pressures and for handling concentrated ferrous chloride solutions. In another application it is being used for the roasting of sulfides to sulfates at a smelter. Titanium has lasted longer in this application than any of the steels which had been used previously. Because of its excellent resistance to white fuming nitric acid it is now being used as a replacement for aluminum in containers for this chemical. Porous titanium filters for use in filtering white and red fuming nitric acid have been produced by powder metallurgy techniques. Corrosion tests on these filters showed a weight loss of only 0.5 per cent in 700 hr immersion in fuming nitric at 160° F as contrasted with complete destruction of materials used previously in less than 175 hr.

Titanium tubing has been installed in processing equipment in a pharmaceutical plant to minimize contamination of the product.

Among other applications in the chemical field are heat exchangers for handling various acid solutions, autoclaves, cooling coils designed to operate under 10,000 psi external pressure at 650° F and processing equipment for handling hot gases.

In the laboratory, the light weight combined with the corrosion resistance of titanium tubing has led to its use as an absorption tube in a microanalytical combustion train. Accuracy is improved by the replacement of a heavy glass tube with a light-weight titanium tube. Titanium tubing has been used also for heating coils in laboratory autoclaves because of the resistance of this material to the wide variety of chemicals being processed in this equipment.

Miscellaneous Applications

A great number of applications for titanium have been suggested which cannot be readily classified under the headings discussed previously. Brief mention of several of these follows and it should be noted that these are future possibilities.

Titanium cathodes can be used in electroplating and electroforming. Dipping in an acid makes the surface passive and as a result the metal becomes electrochemically neutral to aqueous plating baths. Among desirable properties of such cathodes are, the titanium has no effect on the grain size or orientation of a metal plated on it and electrodeposits can be stripped readily from the surface. Among suggested applications are the production of copper foil by electrodeposition from a sulfate bath; the production of electrolytic manganese; and similar operations. In electroforming, copper printing plates have been formed on cathodes made from titanium sponge; by ruling a fine grid on glass with titanium (which marks glass) a pattern can be obtained on which a thin fine-mesh screen can be deposited composed of such metals as copper, nickel, etc.

The high strength/weight ratio of titanium can reduce the weight of a railroad car and reduce the horsepower required to pull it. An additional advantage is the possibility of reducing the size of the journals and journal boxes because of the reduction in weight. One producer of railroad cars estimates that a reduction in overall weight of a car of 1000 lb saves almost $2000 in the cost of journals.

In trailer trucks also the use of titanium would reduce the dead weight and increase the pay load. Here it is estimated that increasing the pay load is worth from $1.50 to $3 per lb of weight saved.

The Future

Jaffee and Blocher in predicting the future applications of titanium note that substitution for aluminum and magnesium can be expected largely in applications at the upper end of the temperature range for which aluminum and magnesium are suitable, that is from about 300 to 400° F.

For room temperature service, they expect that titanium will be substituted for aluminum and magnesium alloys in all applications where corrosion is a factor since the corrosion resistance of titanium is so superior to that of the other two metals.

No substitution will occur where thermal or electrical conductivity is a factor since aluminum is so much higher in conductivity than titanium or in applications where low density is more important than the strength/weight ratio.

They conclude, also, that most of the present applications of stainless steel in aircraft will be taken over eventually by titanium, particularly at temperatures up to 800° F. In their opinion this includes both structural and nonstructural components.

Marine applications of stainless steel, nickel and monel will also be met by titanium alloys while even the bronzes will be replaced when the price of titanium falls somewhat.

Handling of strong oxidizing and organic acids in the process industries, now being done by stainless steels, will be taken over by titanium only if the price is reduced. Similar results can be expected in the case of copper alloys where conductivity is not a factor and corrosion resistance is the major requirement.

In summary, these authors state that large-scale replacement of other materials by titanium and titanium alloys will depend on cost reduction and substantial increased production, both of which will take time. Chief substitutions will be made for stainless steel, aluminum and magnesium alloys in the medium temperature range for aircraft applications, for steel in air-borne and man-borne ordnance equipment and for copper-base and nickel-base alloys in marine applications.

References

Jaffee, R., "New Techniques Tame Titanium," *SAE Jour.*, 34 (Jan., 1954).

Dick, J. N., "Titanium is Vital to the Air Force," *Jour. of Metals*, 133 (Feb., 1953).

Beardman, E. L., "Navy Has Large Titanium Program," *Jour. of Metals*, 138 (Feb., 1953).

Sweet, J. W., "Application of Titanium Sheet-Strip Limited by Presently Available Alloys," *Jour. of Metals*, 143 (Feb., 1953).

Mesick, R. S., "Titanium Evaluated for Ordnance," *Jour. of Metals*, 136 (Feb., 1953).

Reed, N. L., "Titanium in Ordnance," *Proc. Titanium Symposium*, Watertown Arsenal, 8 (Oct. 8, 1952).

Anon., "Hot Forming Titanium," *Modern Metals*, 88 (Nov., 1953).

Jaffee, R. I. and Blocher, Jr., J. M., "The Technology of Titanium," *Modern Metals*, 62 (Aug., 1952).

APPENDIX

GENERAL REFERENCES

Much of the material dealing with the properties and characteristics of the commercial materials was obtained from publications of the producers, particularly the following—

"Titanium," E. I. Du Pont de Nemours & Co.
"Properties of Titanium and Titanium Alloys," Mallory-Sharon Titanium Corp.
"Rem-Cru Titanium Review" published quarterly by Rem-Cru Titanium, Inc.
"Titanium—New Member of the Family of Metals," Superior Tube Co.
"Handbook on Titanium Metal," 7th edition, Titanium Metals Corp. of America.

Finally, this book is a revised and expanded version of Manual 82, "Titanium and Its Alloys," Materials & Methods, May 1952.

INDEX

183